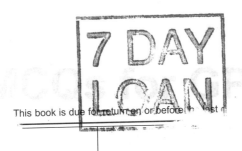
CLINICAL MEDICINE

David R Phillips MA MBBChir MRCP DipGUM

Edited by Laura Percy MA MBBChir MRCP

Published by ISCMedical
Suite 434, Hamilton House, Mabledon Place, London WC1H 9BB
Tel: 0845 226 9487

First Published: January 2006
Second Edition: May 2006
Reprinted November 2006 / March 2007

ISBN13: 978-1-905812-01-1
ISBN10: 1-905812-01-9
A catalogue record for this book is available from the British Library.

The author has, as far as possible, taken care to ensure that the information given in this text is accurate and up to date. However, readers are strongly advised to confirm that the information with regards to specific patient management complies with current legislation, guidelines and local protocols.

The information within this text is intended as a study aid for the purpose of the GPVTS selection examinations. It is not intended, nor should it be used as a medical reference for the direct management of patients or their conditions.

ISCMEDICAL
Interview Skills Consulting

PREFACE

Over the last decade, applications for GPVTS have become more and more competitive. To help select the best applicants, formal assessment with MCQs (Multiple Choice Questions) or EMQs (Extended Matching Questions) alongside interviews are now obligatory for many deaneries. This book aims to give you practice in the types of MCQs you may be faced with.

Candidates are not expected to have highly specialist knowledge. This is an entrance exam into a general training program after all. What is expected is a knowledge base founded from good undergraduate education that has developed with professional experience. In other words, what one would expect of any competent, sensible "House/pre-registration Doctor". For this purpose, the questions attempt to determine whether candidates have indeed taken an active role in their jobs and testing whether candidates are able to demonstrate logical thinking and common sense.

Before you dive into the questions, take a moment to read the following advice. Firstly, I know you have heard it before but, if there is no negative marking then answer every question. Some people still leave questions blank! Next, think about the phraseology of the questions. See below:

Term	Meaning
Pathognomic	A feature which when present is diagnostic for a condition. E.g. Koplik spots in measles.
Characteristic (or typical)	A feature which, if present highly suggests the diagnosis and if absent would lead you to question the diagnosis. Example: Chest pain and myocardial infarction.
Common (or mostly)	A feature that occurs more than 50% of the time. E.g. Productive cough with pneumonia.
Recognised (or associated)	An accepted feature of that disease even if it doesn't occur in every case. E.g. Erythema nodosum and Crohn's colitis

Rare	A feature or condition which one would expect with a low frequency i.e. <1-2%
Specificity	The ability of a test or criteria to pick up a case whilst excluding negatives i.e. few false positives. See below
Specific	A test or criteria which if positive will identify a disease or organism, but no other i.e. few false positives. E.g. Troponin I for myocardial injury.
Sensitivity	The ability of a test or criteria to pick up as many cases as possible without missing any i.e. few false negatives. See below.
Sensitive	A test or criteria that is able to identify cases of a disease. E.g. Amylase in diagnosing pancreatitis.

Understanding the grammar also helps. There was a rhyme at medical school that went: "Never say never nor ever say always". This refers to the fact that, features in medicine rarely occur all of the time or none of the time. With this in mind, statements such as; "Disease X always presents with Y." or "Patients with condition A never have feature B." tend to be false. So if in doubt with such a question, ticking 'false' is a useful strategy. The opposite tends to occur for the words 'may be' or 'can be'. They allow for the possibility that rare exceptions to the rules creep in. Such statements then tend to be true. For example "Cystic fibrosis treatment may involve liver transplantation." This is certainly not the case for every patient but rarely happens and so is true. Since many candidates now catch on to these tricks, examiners try to avoid these terms. However be warned! There are cases when by definition the response MUST be true. For example "Cushing's disease is always caused by an increased secretion of ACTH from the pituitary gland." It must be true since the statement is the definition of Cushing's disease.

Keep these tips in mind and have plenty of practice. That and a good night's sleep before the exam will keep your wits about you. And don't forget to READ THE QUESTION CAREFULLY!

Best of Luck
D.R.P

ISCMEDICAL
Interview Skills Consulting

GLOSSARY

ACE	Angiotensin converting enzyme
ACTH	Adrenocorticotropic hormone
AF	Atrial fibrillation
AIDS	Acquired immunodeficiency syndrome
ALT	Alanine transferase
APTT	Activated partial thromboplastin time
ASD	Atrial septal defect
BMI	Body mass index
bpm	Beats per minute
CABG	Coronary artery bypass graft
CEA	Carcinoembryonic antigen
CRF	Corticotrophin releasing factor
CT	Computed tomography
DVLA	Driver and vehicle licensing agency
ECG	Electrocardiogram
FEV_1	Forced expiratory volume in 1 second
FVC	Forced vital capacity
GTN	Glyceryl trinitrate
HCG	Human chorionic gonadotrophin
HGV	Heavy goods vehicle
HIV	Human immunodeficiency virus
HOCM	Hypertrophic obstructive cardiomyopathy
IHD	Ischaemic heart disease
INR	International normalised ratio
JVP	Jugular venous pressure
KCO	Carbon monoxide transfer co-efficient
LBBB	Left bundle branch block
LDH	Lactate dehydrogenase
MALT	Mucosa associated lymphoid tissue

ISCMEDICAL
Interview Skills Consulting

MEN	Multiple endocrine neoplasia
MI	Myocardial infarction
MRI	Magnetic resonance imaging
MRSA	Methicillin resistant staphylococcus aureus
MUGA	Multiple gate acquisition (scan)
NICE	National institute for clinical excellence
NMDA	N-methyl-D-aspartic acid
NSAID	Non-steroidal anti-inflammatory drug
NYHA	New York heart association
PA	Posterior-anterior
PCR	Polymerase chain reaction
PET	Positron emission tomography
PT	Prothrombin time
RBBB	Right bundle branch block
SIADH	Syndrome of inappropriate antidiuretic hormone secretion
SLE	Systemic lupus erythromatosis
TB	Tuberculosis
tPA	Tissue plasminogen activator
TSH	Thyroid stimulating hormone
VDRL	Venerial disease research laboratory
VMA	Vanillylmandelic acid
VSD	Ventricular septal defect
ZN	Ziehl – Nielsen

CONTENTS

ISCMEDICAL
Interview Skills Consulting

MCQs for GPVTS

CARDIOLOGY

1 Mitral valve prolapse is a recognised association with the following conditions. CARDIO

a. Female with a karyotype XO. True/False

b. Down's syndrome. True/False

c. Osteogenesis imperfecta. True/False

d. Pseudoxanthoma elasticum. True/False

e. Marfan's syndrome. True/False

2 Indications for cardiac catheterisation include: CARDIO

a. Assessment of primary pulmonary hypertension. True/False

b. Assessment of valvular heart disease. True/False

c. Treatment of congenital heart defects. True/False

d. Endomyocardial biopsy. True/False

e. Electrophysiological studies and pacing. True/False

3 Trans-oesophageal echocardiography (TOE). **CARDIO**

a. May be contraindicated in cervical rheumatoid arthritis. True/False

b. Is better than trans-thoracic echocardiography for assessing aortic root pathology. True/False

c. Is the first imaging modality of choice to assess left atrial myxoma. True/False

d. Is traditionally the method for showing M mode depictions of prosthetic valves. True/False

e. Involves the use of lignocaine (lidocaine) spray. True/False

4 Imaging in cardiology. **CARDIO**

a. MRI is useful for guidance of pacing wires. True/False

b. PET can uncover areas of 'hibernating' myocardium with the potential to recover after revascularisation surgery. True/False

c. MUGA scanning uses radio-isotopes to diagnose extent of IHD. True/False

d. Dobutamine is used to stress the heart during functional scanning. True/False

e. Tuberculous pericarditis requires CT or other 3-D imaging to secure the diagnosis. True/False

| 5 | Angina. | CARDIO |

a. Prinzmetal variant is commonly brought on with changes in posture.   True/False

b. Nitrates should be given in such a dosing to give 24 hour coverage.   True/False

c. If cholesterol is greater than 4.3 mmol/L, a statin should be commenced regardless of other risk factors.   True/False

d. Sublingual spray is better than nitrate tablets in the elderly.   True/False

e. Nicorandil can cause headaches and so the dose may have to be reduced.   True/False

| 6 | Coronary angioplasty. | CARDIO |

a. NICE recommends stenting after all balloon angioplasties.   True/False

b. Antiplatelet drugs are usually indicated post stenting to reduce stenosis.   True/False

c. Drug coated stents are indicated to prevent stent slippage.   True/False

d. Is better than CABG for symptom control in diabetics.   True/False

e. Is better than CABG for distal vessel disease.   True/False

7	Acute coronary syndrome.	**CARDIO**

a. Includes MI, unstable angina and coronary vasospasm.   True/False

b. Is diagnosed if an appropriate history of pain is given and   True/False
   new onset LBBB is noticed.

c. May be excluded if the ST segment falls.   True/False

d. In acute management, morphine and metoclopramide i.m.   True/False
   are often given.

e. Tirofiban can be used as an alternative to coronary   True/False
   angioplasty.

8	Temporary pacing post MI should be undertaken urgently in:	**CARDIO**

a. First degree block.   True/False

b. Wenckebach (Mobitz I).   True/False

c. Inferior MI with rate of 48 bpm.   True/False

d. Trifascicular block.   True/False

e. Mobitz II block.   True/False

ISCMEDICAL
Interview Skills Consulting

| 9 | Post MI complications. | CARDIO |

a. Right ventricular failure tends to respond to fluid replacement.　　True/False

b. Dressler's syndrome can be treated with steroids.　　True/False

c. A left ventricular aneurysm usually presents at weeks 4-6.　　True/False

d. Pericarditic pain classically eases on sitting forward.　　True/False

e. Tamponade is characterised by Beck's triad of raised JVP, hypotension and muffled heart sounds.　　True/False

| 10 | Dysrhythmias | CARDIO |

a. A bradycardia won't require treament if the heart rate is above 40 bpm.　　True/False

b. Can be provoked by doxorubicin.　　True/False

c. An ECG should always be taken to aid diagnosis.　　True/False

d. Verapamil, beta blockers, amiodarone or flecainide can be used in post MI atrial fibrillation.　　True/False

e. Wide complex tachycardias only arise from the ventricle.　　True/False

11 Heart failure. **CARDIO**

a. Can be exacerbated by NSAIDs. True/False

b. Metolazone is a potassium sparing diuretic. True/False

c. ECG and b-type natriuretic peptide precede True/False
echocardiography in diagnosis of heart failure.

d. Beta blockers are contraindicated. True/False

e. NYHA class III involves comfort at rest but dyspnoea on less True/False
than ordinary activities.

12 The following are recognised causes of hypertension. **CARDIO**

a. Addison's syndrome. True/False

b. Chronic pyelonephritis. True/False

c. Mycrogynon 30. True/False

d. Systemic sclerosis. True/False

e. Ankylosing spondylitis. True/False

7

13 Hypertension. CARDIO

a. Korotkoff V is often used to assess blood pressure in pregnancy. True/False

b. Grade one retinopathy is characterised by silver wiring of retinal arteries. True/False

c. Papilloedema often indicates malignant hypertension. True/False

d. Calcium channel blockers are first line in those with ankle oedema. True/False

e. Thiazide diuretics are first choice antihypertensives in most patients. True/False

14 Hypertension therapy. CARDIO

a. Younger patients are best commenced on a beta blocker or an ACE inhibitor. True/False

b. In malignant hypertension, sublingual nifedipine is easily tolerated and reversible. True/False

c. Headache and limb weakness in malignant hypertension is an indication to begin intravenous therapy with arterial line monitoring. True/False

d. Young black patients are best treated with beta blockers as first line agents. True/False

e. Sodium nitroprusside has potential arsenic toxicity. True/False

15 | Interpreting the exercise tolerance test. | **CARDIO**

a. Is made simpler in LBBB. | True/False

b. Is affected by the direction of the ST slope. | True/False

c. May lead to false positives in a fifth of middle aged women. | True/False

d. With 1mm J point depression, it is almost diagnostic of 2-3 vessel disease. | True/False

e. May be futile if the patient is taking metoprolol. | True/False

16 | The following can lead to high output heart failure. | **CARDIO**

a. Pregnancy. | True/False

b. Beri Beri. | True/False

c. Paget's disease. | True/False

d. Thyrotoxicosis. | True/False

e. Arterio-venous fistulas. | True/False

9

17 Myocardial disease.   `CARDIO`

a. Myxoma is a rare malignancy of the myocardium which   True/False
    gives a characteristic 'plop' sound on auscultation when
    projecting from the left atrium into the mitral ring.

b. Amyloid can cause restrictive cardiomyopathy.   True/False

c. Alcohol can give a classic 'flabby' heart or dilated   True/False
    cardiomyopathy.

d. HOCM is an autosomal dominant condition which can cause   True/False
    sudden cardiac death.

e. An ejection systolic murmur which decreases on squatting is   True/False
    characteristic of HOCM.

18 Pericarditis.   `CARDIO`

a. Is an indication for dialysis in acute renal failure.   True/False

b. Is seen in rheumatoid arthritis but not in SLE.   True/False

c. Ibuprofen is first line management.   True/False

d. Positive ZN stain from pericardiocentesis is diagnostic of TB.   True/False

e. Nocardia characteristically leads to it.   True/False

19 Prophylaxis for endocarditis should be given to: **CARDIO**

a. Patients with patent ductus arteriosus.   True/False

b. Patients with mitral valve prolapse complicated by mitral   True/False
regurgitation.

c. Those undergoing cardiac catheterisation.   True/False

d. Those undergoing caesarian section.   True/False

e. Those undergoing sclerotherapy of oesophageal varices.   True/False

20 Consider surgery for infective endocarditis if: **CARDIO**

a. All Duke's criteria are met.   True/False

b. Fungal endocarditis.   True/False

c. Lengthening PR interval on ECG.   True/False

d. MRSA bacteraemia.   True/False

e. Janeway lesions and Osler nodes are seen.   True/False

21 Infective endocarditis.   CARDIO

a. Is commonly associated with 'HACEK' organisms   True/False

b. 50% of cases occur on native, normal valves.   True/False

c. Endocarditis on abnormal valves tends to give an acute presentation.   True/False

d. Enteric organisms suggest bowel malignancy.   True/False

e. Can be diagnosed in the absence of any positive blood cultures.   True/False

22 Mitral stenosis.   CARDIO

a. Dysphagia and recurrent laryngeal nerve palsy are recognised consequences of severe stenosis.   True/False

b. Can lead to a Graham Steel murmur.   True/False

c. Stenosis is more severe with increasing length of diastolic murmur.   True/False

d. DC cardioversion is an alternative to rate control for AF.   True/False

e. The severity of the murmur is associated with a louder opening snap.   True/False

| 23 | Causes of bradycardia include: | CARDIO |

a. Cushing reflex.   True/False

b. Amiodarone.   True/False

c. Cholestasis.   True/False

d. Carbimazole.   True/False

e. Athletic lifestyle.   True/False

| 24 | Mitral valve disease. | CARDIO |

a. Is most commonly associated with functional dilatation and ischaemic heart disease in the UK.   True/False

b. Balloon valvuloplasty is particularly effective for calcified mitral stenosis.   True/False

c. Marfan's syndrome leading to large vessel disease and dissection is a recognised cause.   True/False

d. Malar flush is pathognomic of mitral stenosis.   True/False

e. AF arising from left atrial dilatation is commonly seen.   True/False

25	The following can lead to long QT syndrome.	CARDIO

a. Ischaemic heart disease.   True/False

b. Hypermagnesaemia.   True/False

c. Erythromycin.   True/False

d. Hypocalcuria.   True/False

e. Ciprofloxacin.   True/False

26	Right axis deviation on an ECG can be caused by:	CARDIO

a. Pulmonary embolism.   True/False

b. Systemic hypertension.   True/False

c. Wolf Parkinson White.   True/False

d. Pulmonary hypertension.   True/False

e. Anterolateral myocardial infarction.   True/False

27	Regarding the ECG.	CARDIO

a. P waves are always absent in nodal rhythms.   True/False

b. Absence of a P wave is characteristic of AF.   True/False

c. A short PR interval implies atrial-ventricular block.   True/False

d. P mitrale indicates right atrial hypertrophy.   True/False

e. Digoxin can cause ST depression.   True/False

28	Cardiac surgery.	CARDIO

a. Balloon valvuloplasty is contraindicated in mixed mitral valve disease.   True/False

b. Valvotomy is almost exclusively performed as an open heart surgery.   True/False

c. Tissue valves are ideal in elderly patients.   True/False

d. After tissue valve replacement of the mitral valve, warfarin anticoagulation is almost never required.   True/False

e. An aortic murmur 6 months post metalic aortic valve replacement should prompt an urgent assessment by a cardiologist.   True/False

29 Aortic valve disease.   `CARDIO`

a. Pulse pressure is a key sign to severity of disease.   True/False

b. Valve gradient of > 50 mmHg is an indication to consider   True/False
    surgery in aortic stenosis.

c. Carotid radiation of murmur can distinguish stenosis from   True/False
    sclerosis.

d. Aortic regurgitation post MI should prompt urgent aortic root True/False
    assessment and possible surgery.

e. Is a complication of spondyloarthropathy.   True/False

30 Tricuspid regurgitation.   `CARDIO`

a. Is a feature of primary pulmonary hypertension.   True/False

b. Is a recognised feature of staphylococcal endocarditis.   True/False

c. May cause a five-fold rise in the ALT.   True/False

d. Causes giant 'a' waves in the JVP.   True/False

e. Has a characteristic pan-diastolic murmur.   True/False

31 Pulmonary embolism   **CARDIO**

a. An echocardiogram can be diagnostic.   True/False

b. RBBB with right ventricular strain can be found on ECG.   True/False

c. $S_I Q_{III} T_{III}$ pattern on the ECG is commonly seen.   True/False

d. The patient can be bradycardic.   True/False

e. May lead to AF.   True/False

---

32 Congenital heart disease.   **CARDIO**

a. ASD may only present in later life when it commonly leads to   True/False
    paradoxical emboli.

b. VSD is the most common heart defect found in adults.   True/False

c. ASD in adults should on the whole only be treated if   True/False
    symptoms persist because they otherwise tend to close
    spontaneously.

d. If untreated, coarctation of the aorta can lead to   True/False
    Eisenmenger's syndrome.

e. Coarctation of the aorta is a recognised feature of   True/False
    Kleinfelter's syndrome.

33 Causes of a long PR interval include · **CARDIO**

a. Romano Ward syndrome. · True/False

b. Infective endocarditis with abscess formation. · True/False

c. Sarcoidosis. · True/False

d. Leptospirosis. · True/False

e. Borrelia burgdorferri. · True/False

34 Advice following myocardial infarction includes: · **CARDIO**

a. Taking a month off work. · True/False

b. If holding an HGV licence, must not drive for 3 months and then complete 3 stages of a Bruce exercise tolerance test being off antianginals for the previous 24hours. · True/False

c. Normal driving licence holders to refrain from driving for 3 months. · True/False

d. Not to have sex until they can complete 2 stages (6 minutes) of a Bruce protocol exercise test. · True/False

e. To keep a GTN spray or tablets at hand at all times. · True/False

35 Regarding the ECG.   **CARDIO**

a. Lead V5 is placed at the anterior axillary line.   True/False

b. RBBB is characterised by a QRS of > 0.12s, with first stroke   True/False
being positive in V1 (rSR pattern).

c. Bifascicular block is characterised by RBBB and LBBB.   True/False

d. Trifascicular block is characterised by bifascicular block and   True/False
first degree heart block.

e. Right atrial hypertophy can be determined by large P waves   True/False
in leads II and V1.

36 Tall R waves in lead V1 on an ECG are characteristic of the   **CARDIO**
following:

a. Hypertrophic obstructive cardiomyopathy.   True/False

b. Wolff Parkinson White type B.   True/False

c. Dextrocardia.   True/False

d. External cardiac pacing.   True/False

e. Left ventricular hypertrophy.   True/False

ISCMEDICAL
Interview Skills Consulting

37 Driving and heart disease.   **CARDIO**

a. DVLA must be informed if pacemaker inserted.   True/False

b. DVLA must be informed if angina occurs at rest.   True/False

c. DVLA must be informed if hypertension over 160/100   True/False
    mmHg.

d. Must stop driving for a week after angioplasty or pacemaker   True/False
    implant.

e. Must abstain from driving for 6months after first   True/False
    cardioverter/defibrillator implanted or delivered treatment.

38 Contraindications to an exercise tolerance test include: **CARDIO**

a. Unstable angina.   True/False

b. Uncontrolled heart failure.   True/False

c. Severe aortic stenosis.   True/False

d. Permanent pacemaker in situ.   True/False

e. Osteoarthritis.   True/False

MCQs for GPVTS

ENDOCRINOLOGY

39 | **Causes of hypopituitarism include:** | **ENDO**

a. Retinoblastoma. .... True/False

b. Craniopharyngioma. .... True/False

c. Prolactinoma. .... True/False

d. Acromegaly. .... True/False

e. Phaeochromocytoma .... True/False

40 | **Diabetes mellitus.** | **ENDO**

a. A random glucose test under 11.1mmol/l excludes diabetes.   True/False

b. All those with impaired fasting glucose should undergo an oral glucose tolerance test.   True/False

c. Screening by detecting glycosuria is highly sensitive but poorly specific for diabetes mellitus.   True/False

d. Women with gestational diabetes are at increased risk of developing diabetes in later life.   True/False

e. Type 2 diabetes in more common in Asians than Caucasians.   True/False

41	Diabetes mellitus.	ENDO

a. During periods of viral illness when caloric intake falls, insulin dose should be decreased.   True/False

b. Ketoacidosis is unlikely to be caused by type 2 diabetes.   True/False

c. Diabetic coma occurs with hypoglycaemia and not hyperglycaemia.   True/False

d. Patients have been shown to have better glycaemic control when on strict regular insulin dosing and regimented dietary plans.   True/False

e. In ketoacidosis, rehydration takes precedence over insulin administration.   True/False

42	The following is true regarding thyroid hormones.	ENDO

a. The thyroid excretes mainly T4.   True/False

b. T4 is more active than T3.   True/False

c. Only protein bound hormone is active.   True/False

d. TSH is high in primary hyperthyroidism   True/False

e. TSH is high in secondary (pituitary) hyperthyroidism.   True/False

43 Thyroid disease   **ENDO**

a. Sick euthyroid syndrome refers to subclinical hypothyroidism   True/False
   which decompensates during illness, requiring subsequent
   thyroid replacement if it persists.

b. A normal free T4 or T3 can rule out hypothyroidism.   True/False

c. Patients with pernicious anaemia must be screened for   True/False
   thyroid disease.

d. Hypothyroidism can cause proximal myopathy.   True/False

e. Hypothyroidism is rare over the age of 70.   True/False

44 The following thyroid function results are correctly matched **ENDO**
    to the disorder.

a. High TSH and normal T4: Sublinical or compensated   True/False
   thyrotoxicosis.

b. Low TSH and low T4: Primary hypothyroidism.   True/False

c. 'Hot' nodule on ultrasound scan: likely malignant tumour.   True/False

d. Positive thyroid-stimulating immunoglobulin: autoimmune   True/False
   hypothyroidism.

e. High TSH and low T4: Primary hypothyroidism.   True/False

45	The following are recognised features of hyperthyroidism.	ENDO

a. Labial mood.   True/False

b. Bladder incontinence.   True/False

c. Dysmenorrhoea.   True/False

d. Hyperphagia.   True/False

e. Heart failure.   True/False

46	The following are commonly recognised presentations of types of diabetic neuropathy.	ENDO

a. Burning uncomfortable pain in limbs especially in bed at   True/False
   night.

b. Postural hypotension   True/False

c. Vomiting   True/False

d. Loss of muscle bulk and weakness in thigh muscles   True/False

e. Double vision   True/False

47	Diabetes insipidis (DI)	ENDO

a. Is confirmed by abnormally low urine osmolality following a water deprivation test. True/False

b. Cranial DI can be caused by lithium administration. True/False

c. Is treated by fluid restriction. True/False

d. Can be mimicked by alcohol consumption. True/False

e. Is suggested in any patient with a plasma sodium >140mmol/l. True/False

48	Diabetes insipidis (DI) is associated with	ENDO

a. Vitiligo. True/False

b. Head injury. True/False

c. Sarcoidosis. True/False

d. Respiratory tract infections. True/False

e. Pancreatic carcinoma. True/False

49 Acromegaly. **ENDO**

a. Is rare before the age of 30. True/False

b. Can be confirmed if serum growth hormone suppresses in response to the insulin tolerance test. True/False

c. Can be diagnosed by raised growth hormone levels. True/False

d. Excess sweating indicates active disease. True/False

e. Causes increased cranial bone growth which leads to a prominent supraorbital ridge and prognathism. True/False

50 Diabetic foot disease. **ENDO**

a. Most patients have either neuropathy or arteriopathy. True/False

b. Temperature sensation is often the first modality to be lost in neuropathy. True/False

c. Ulcers tend to be shallow. True/False

d. X-ray is obligatory when assessing a patient with an infected foot ulcer. True/False

e. Claudication symptoms are rare or 'silent' in diabetics. True/False

51	HbA1c	ENDO

a. May give a false impression of glycaemic control in sickle cell patients.   True/False

b. Can give a false impression of glycaemic control in those with macrocytic anaemias.   True/False

c. Is a reliable measure of glycaemic control over periods of a few weeks in duration, during pregnancy.   True/False

d. Remains high in some patients despite strict glycaemic control.   True/False

e. A high value suggests increasing chances of vascular complications.   True/False

52	Insulin resistance is a feature of the following.	ENDO

a. Acromegaly.   True/False

b. Polycystic ovarian syndrome.   True/False

c. Addison's disease.   True/False

d. Whipple's disease.   True/False

e. Chronic pancreatitis.   True/False

53 Pituitary tumours. **ENDO**

a. Up to 15% are malignant. True/False

b. Up to a third produce no hormone. True/False

c. CT of the pituitary fossa is the best investigation. True/False

d. Surgery, often with the transphenoidal approach, is the treatment of choice in most. True/False

e. Radiotherapy is contraindicated. True/False

54 The following can be associated with hyperprolactinaemia. **ENDO**

a. Chlorpromazine. True/False

b. Sarcoidosis. True/False

c. Carcinoid syndrome. True/False

d. Cushing's disease. True/False

e. Pregnancy. True/False

55 Recognised features of androgen deficiency in a man are: **ENDO**

a. Decreased ejaculate volume.   True/False

b. Decreased aggression.   True/False

c. Loss of all body hair.   True/False

d. Decreased muscle bulk.   True/False

e. Dry skin.   True/False

56 Recognised causes of gynaecomastia include: **ENDO**

a. Cocaine.   True/False

b. Canabis.   True/False

c. Puberty.   True/False

d. Spironolactone.   True/False

e. Digoxin.   True/False

57	The following causes of erectile dysfunction are recognised indications for treatment with sildenafil.	ENDO

a. Parkinson's disease.   True/False

b. End stage renal failure.   True/False

c. Multiple sclerosis.   True/False

d. Renal dialysis.   True/False

e. Hypertension.   True/False

58	The following is true regarding Conn's syndrome.	ENDO

a. Hypertension with palpitations and flushing is common.   True/False

b. Hyperkalaemia is often noted.   True/False

c. The source is an adenoma arising from the glamerulosa cells of the adrenal gland.   True/False

d. Urinary VMA is often raised.   True/False

e. Surgery with pre-operative alpha blockade is a treatment option.   True/False

59 The following are recognised features of Addison's disease.   ENDO

a. Diarrhoea and vomiting.   True/False

b. Myalgia.   True/False

c. Anorexia.   True/False

d. Cough.   True/False

e. Ankle oedema.   True/False

60 Addison's disease.   ENDO

a. In the UK over three quarters if due to autoimmune disease. True/False

b. TB is a significant cause.   True/False

c. Can quickly lead to coma and death in acute cases.   True/False

d. A 24-hour urine collection can aid diagnosis.   True/False

e. Glucocorticosteroids are sufficient to treat adrenal failure. True/False

61	Cushing's syndrome.	ENDO

a. A cortisol taken at midnight is the best screening test.　　　True/False

b. Stimulation of cortisol production with a synthetic ACTH can　True/False
unmask Cushing's syndrome.

c. Cushing's disease is confirmed by identification of adrenal　True/False
adenomas.

d. An undetectable plasma ACTH makes an adrenal tumour　True/False
very likely.

e. A reduction of ACTH in response to high dose　　　　　True/False
dexamethasone suggests a pituitary adenoma as the source
of ACTH.

62	The following are recognised causes of 'Pseudocushing's' disease.	ENDO

a. Cocaine abuse.　　　　　　　　　　　　　　　　True/False

b. Alcohol excess.　　　　　　　　　　　　　　　　True/False

c. BMI > 35 kg/m2.　　　　　　　　　　　　　　　True/False

d. Familial hypertriglyceridaemias.　　　　　　　　　　True/False

e. Osteoporosis.　　　　　　　　　　　　　　　　True/False

63 The following are features of Cushing's syndrome.   ENDO

a. Menstrual irregularities.   True/False

b. Purple abdominal striae.   True/False

c. Accelerated wound healing.   True/False

d. Peripheral oedema.   True/False

e. Hyponatraemia.   True/False

64 The following are recognised causes of Cushing's syndrome.   ENDO

a. A CRF producing pituitary adenoma.   True/False

b. Ectopic ACTH production.   True/False

c. A squamous cell lung carcinoma.   True/False

d. A carcinoma of the adrenal cortex.   True/False

e. Long term prednisolone therapy.   True/False

65 Hyperparathyroidism   **ENDO**

a. Most commonly presents with renal stones.   True/False

b. The increased osteoclastic activity leads to osteomalacia.   True/False

c. The priority in severe hypercalcaemia is administering a   True/False
   calcium reducing agent e.g. a bisphosphonate.

d. Tertiary hyperparathyroidism is only seen following   True/False
   secondary hyperparathyroidism.

e. Hyperparathyroidism occurs in both MEN 1 and 2.   True/False

66 Drugs and hyperthyroidism.   **ENDO**

a. Carbimazole can cross the placenta.   True/False

b. Priority of treatment is with beta blockade if symptomatic. True/False

c. Carbimazole is contraindicated in asthmatics.   True/False

d. Carbimazole can cause bone marrow suppression.   True/False

e. Many patients may at some point need thyroxine therapy.   True/False

67 The following are recognised causes of hyperthyroidism.　　**ENDO**

a. Hashimoto's thyroiditis.　　　　　　　　　　　　　　True/False

b. De Quervain's thyroiditis.　　　　　　　　　　　　　True/False

c. Grave's thyroiditis.　　　　　　　　　　　　　　　　True/False

d. Antiarrhythmic medication.　　　　　　　　　　　　True/False

e. Malignant (adenocarcinoma) of the thyroid gland.　　True/False

68 Investigations for a routine diabetic follow up should include:　**ENDO**

a. Retinal photography.　　　　　　　　　　　　　　　True/False

b. 24-hour urine collection.　　　　　　　　　　　　　True/False

c. Glomerular filtration rate.　　　　　　　　　　　　True/False

d. ECG.　　　　　　　　　　　　　　　　　　　　　True/False

e. Serum lipid analysis.　　　　　　　　　　　　　　True/False

Interview Skills Consulting

Mcqs for GPVTS

GASTROENTEROLOGY

69 Alcohol withdrawal.   **GASTRO**

a. Chlormethiazole is now the preferred alternative to   True/False
   chlordiazepoxide.

b. Delerium tremens presents 12 hours after abstinence.   True/False

c. Diazepam should be avoided.   True/False

d. Hallucinations tend to be tactile rather than visual.   True/False

e. Formication is usually attributed to hysteria.   True/False

70 Mallory-Weiss tear.   **GASTRO**

a. Rarely occurs only once in patients.   True/False

b. Frequently occurs in the presence of Barrett's oesophagus.   True/False

c. Rarely requires endoscopy.   True/False

d. A proton pump inhibitor is a recognised treatment.   True/False

e. Should be treated by sclerotherapy if vomiting continues   True/False
   after initial presentation.

71 Vitamin deficiencies. **GASTRO**

a. B1 deficiency can lead to heart failure. True/False

b. Beri Beri is often characterised by "Dermatitis, Diarrhoea, Dementia & Death". True/False

c. Pellagra can be precipitated by anti TB medications. True/False

d. Vitamin A deficiency leads to night blindness. True/False

e. Vitamin A is safely treated by super-supplementation. True/False

72 The following are recognised features of scurvy (vitamin C deficiency). **GASTRO**

a. Dry skin. True/False

b. Hallitosis. True/False

c. Haemorrhage from hair follicles. True/False

d. Upper respiratory tract infections. True/False

e. Haemarthrosis. True/False

73 Altered bowel habit. **GASTRO**

a. A rectal examination can be deferred if the patient has just evacuated the rectum.　True/False

b. Constipation can be caused by irritable bowel syndrome.　True/False

c. Tenesmus is an indication for lower bowel endoscopy.　True/False

d. Iron tablets can cause constipation.　True/False

e. Can result from mesenteric ischaemia.　True/False

74 Jaundice. **GASTRO**

a. Bilirubin is conjugated in the liver to make it water soluble.　True/False

b. Urobilinogen comes from the formation of urinary bilinogen within the kidneys.　True/False

c. Stercobilin is a bilirubin by-product that gives faeces its dark pigmentation.　True/False

d. Gilbert's syndrome is a benign cause of jaundice which can cause transient jaundice in times of starvation.　True/False

e. Haemolytic anaemia can lead to prehepatic (unconjugated) jaundice.　True/False

75	Gastric ulcers.	GASTRO

a. Are mostly found in the elderly.   True/False

b. Are twice as common as duodenal ulcers.   True/False

c. Are a recognised complication of pancreatitis.   True/False

d. Are a recognised complication of severe burns.   True/False

e. Are more likely to be malignant if on the greater curve of the   True/False
   stomach.

76	Acute upper gastrointestinal bleeding.	GASTRO

a. The first priority is to gain venous access and replace   True/False
   volume loss.

b. In an emergency, group O Rh +ve can be given.   True/False

c. The Rockall risk score is a useful prognostic tool to guide   True/False
   further management.

d. Is a certainty if a patient has 'coffee ground' vomit.   True/False

e. Is often associated with a raised serum urea.   True/False

77 Management of gastro-oesophageal reflux disease involves: **GASTRO**

a. Recommending wearing less tight clothes.   True/False

b. Avoiding bisphophonates.   True/False

c. Avoiding eating within 3 hours of bedtime.   True/False

d. Sleeping on one's side in bed.   True/False

e. Considering metoclopramide.   True/False

78 Hiatus hernia.   **GASTRO**

a. Rolling is more common than sliding type.   True/False

b. Can be visualised on plain chest X-ray.   True/False

c. Can lead to a chronic cough.   True/False

d. Should be treated with surgery if any symptoms appear.   True/False

e. Around 75% are symptomatic.   True/False

79 Dyspepsia. **GASTRO**

a. A four-week history of dyspepsia unresponsive to antacids in   True/False
    a 35 year old should prompt a referral to endoscopy.

b. Patients with H.pylori despite resolution of symptoms with   True/False
    'triple therapy' should be routinely referred for endoscopy.

c. Serology for H.pylori is a useful follow-up tool to assess   True/False
    response to treatment.

d. ^{13}C-urea breath tests have been superceded by serology for   True/False
    H.pylori.

e. Patients over 55 years with dyspepsia should be referred   True/False
    straight to endoscopy.

80 Management of ulcerative colitis (UC). **GASTRO**

a. Steroid therapy is reserved for moderate to severe cases.   True/False

b. In severe cases, low molecular weight heparin (LMWH)   True/False
    should be considered.

c. Azathioprine is given in those who can't tolerate steroids or   True/False
    who rapidly deteriorate when steroids are weaned.

d. Sulfasalazine can lead to oligospermia.   True/False

e. Cyclosporin causes anaemia and blood levels must be   True/False
    monitored.

81	Common associations with peptic ulcer disease include:	GASTRO

a. Smoking.   True/False

b. Ibuprofen and diclofenac.   True/False

c. Zollinger Ellison syndrome.   True/False

d. Corticosteroid therapy.   True/False

e. Gastrinoma of pancreatic cells.   True/False

82	Liver failure.	GASTRO

a. Acute failure is most commonly caused by recent insult to the liver such as toxins or virus.   True/False

b. Wilson's disease and autoimmune hepatitis cause chronic hepatitis but are unlikely to lead to decompensated liver failure.   True/False

c. Change in mood is sufficient to suspect encephalopathy.   True/False

d. Hyperglycaemia is a common complication.   True/False

e. Exogenous protein should be limited. Albumin under 30 facilitates recovery.   True/False

83 | Ulcerative colitis (UC). | **GASTRO**

a. Cigarette smoking is thought to be protective.   True/False

b. Is associated with seronegative arthritis.   True/False

c. Diarrhoea and fever suggest infective causes rather than UC.   True/False

d. Risk of colonic carcinoma is enhanced in UC.   True/False

e. Abdominal film is essential in a young person presenting   True/False
with acute bloody diarrhoea.

84 | Crohn's sisease. | **GASTRO**

a. Is more common in the terminal ileum and proximal colon.   True/False

b. Malabsorption is less common than in ulcerative colitis (UC).   True/False

c. Is characterised by pseudopolyps in the colon.   True/False

d. Monoclonal antibodies are to be considered in cases where   True/False
steroids are problematic.

e. Daily methotrexate is useful in some patients.   True/False

85 | Irritable bowel syndrome (IBS). | **GASTRO**

a. Coeliac serology is unecessary in a 20 year old presenting   True/False
with classical IBS symptoms.

b. Patients over 45 should be considered for colonoscopy   True/False
before IBS is diagnosed.

c. If pain timing is cyclical, then a gynaecology referral is worth   True/False
considering in women.

d. Lactulose is contraindicated in many patients.   True/False

e. Will resolve spontaneously in the majority with appropriate   True/False
dietary measures.

86 | Recognised treatments for irritable bowel syndrome include: | **GASTRO**

a. High fibre diet.   True/False

b. Loperamide.   True/False

c. Hypnotherapy.   True/False

d. Metronidazole.   True/False

e. Elemental diet.   True/False

87	Pancreatic cancer.	GASTRO

a. Most commonly arises in the body or tail and so obstructive jaundice is a late feature.　　True/False

b. Tumours in the head of the pancreas tend to give epigastric pain.　　True/False

c. CA19-9 is a specific marker of disease.　　True/False

d. Endoscopic retrograde cholangio-pancreatography is more sensitive than magnetic resonance imaging.　　True/False

e. Chemotherapy has a limited role, restricted to adjuvant treatment post pancreatectomy.　　True/False

88	Diarrhoea	GASTRO

a. Refers to more than 6 soft to loose stools per day.　　True/False

b. The presence of mucus in stool will exclude irritable bowel syndrome (IBS).　　True/False

c. Fatty stool suggests large bowel pathology.　　True/False

d. Faecal occult bloods are a specific test for colonic carcinoma in patients over 60.　　True/False

e. Codeine is routinely given once stool cultures are sent.　　True/False

89 Recognised associations of primary biliary cirrhosis include: **GASTRO**

a. Systemic sclerosis (scleroderma). True/False

b. Autoimmune thyroid disease. True/False

c. Rheumatoid arthritis. True/False

d. Alopecia areata. True/False

e. Primary pulmonary hypertension. True/False

90 Oesophageal varices. **GASTRO**

a. During resuscitation, blood pressure can fall sharply and so the systolic blood pressure should be maintained at 130mmHg or higher. True/False

b. Sclerotherapy is not used in prophylaxis, it is reserved for acute therapy. True/False

c. Beta blockers should be considered as first line for asymptomatic varices. True/False

d. Glypressin or terlipressin are now accepted as part of the acute management of bleeding varices along with resuscitation. True/False

e. If medical therapy fails, then a Sengstaken-Blakemore tube should be placed whilst awaiting arrival of senior/specialist help. True/False

91	Cirrhosis.	GASTRO

a. Development of hepatocellular carcinoma (HCC) is most significantly associated with hepatitis B virus. True/False

b. Although quite rare, can be caused by hepatitis E virus. True/False

c. Is reversible in the first year. True/False

d. Can be caused by digoxin. True/False

e. Chronic alcohol abuse is second only to viral hepatitis as the leading UK cause. True/False

92	Endoscopy.	GASTRO

a. Sigmoidoscopy views the rectum only. True/False

b. Proton pump inhibitors can mask up to a third of adenocarcinomas otherwise detectable on endoscopy. True/False

c. Sigmoidoscopy requires up to 2 sachets of oral laxative before procedure. True/False

d. Antibiotic prophylaxis is indicated before endoscopic retrograde cholangiopancreatography (ERCP). True/False

e. Mortality for ERCP is around 1-2%. True/False

93 | Primary biliary cirrhosis (PBC). | **GASTRO**

a. Osteomalacia is common.   True/False

b. Is more common in women than men.   True/False

c. Is most often picked up on investigation for incidental   True/False
    jaundice.

d. Anti-smooth muscle antibodies (SMA) are specific to PBC.   True/False

e. Severe pruritis is an indication for liver transplantation.   True/False

94 | Recognised features of Wilson's disease include: | **GASTRO**

a. Kayser Fleischer rings on the cornea.   True/False

b. Disinhibition   True/False

c. Dystonias.   True/False

d. Haemolysis.   True/False

e. Increased serum caeruloplasmin.   True/False

95	The following are recognised features of hereditary haemochromatosis.	GASTRO

a. Arthropathy.   True/False

b. Diabetes.   True/False

c. Uveitis.   True/False

d. Cardiomyopathy.   True/False

e. Glomerulonephritis.   True/False

96	Regarding liver tumours.	GASTRO

a. Most liver tumours present with hepatomegaly.   True/False

b. The majority of hepatocellular carcinoma (HCC) have a raised alpha fetoprotein.   True/False

c. Surgery and chemotherapy are options for liver tumours.   True/False

d. Haemangiomas, if detected on imaging, require prompt referral to hepatobiliary surgeons.   True/False

e. HCC is common in those from South America.   True/False

97 The following are associations of coeliac disease.   **GASTRO**

a. HLA DR3.   True/False

b. Seborrhoeic dermatitis.   True/False

c. Steatorrhoea.   True/False

d. Gastrointestinal T cell lymphoma.   True/False

e. Oesophageal carcinoma.   True/False

98 The following are recognised causes of malabsorption.   **GASTRO**

a. Pharyngeal pouch.   True/False

b. Cystic fibrosis.   True/False

c. Post-vagotomy.   True/False

d. Thyrotoxicosis.   True/False

e. Diverticular disease.   True/False

99 Oral disease.   **GASTRO**

a. Candida is a commensal organism carried in the mouths of about half of the population.   True/False

b. Cheilitis or angular stomatitis is associated with folate or vitamin B deficiency.   True/False

c. Most cases of gingivitis are associated with an underlying immune deficiency.   True/False

d. A patient with microstomia should be assessed for oesophageal reflux and Raynaud's disease.   True/False

e. Macroglossia is associated with iron and folate deficiency.   True/False

100 Dysphagia.   **GASTRO**

a. This is painful swallowing, the causes of which can be benign or malignant.   True/False

b. History of regurgitation and neck swelling suggest an oesophageal pouch.   True/False

c. After blood tests and chest X-ray, endoscopy is the next line investigation.   True/False

d. Achalasia is primarily a motility disorder which can be treated by endoscopic surgery.   True/False

e. Can be a consequence of mitral stenosis.   True/False

101 The following are recognised causes of dysphagia.   **GASTRO**

a. Candidiasis.   True/False

b. Motor neurone disease.   True/False

c. Botulism.   True/False

d. Proton pump inhibitors.   True/False

e. Undergoing bronchoscopy.   True/False

102 Jaundice.   **GASTRO**

a. Pale stools are always due to obstructive jaundice.   True/False

b. Dark black stools almost always indicate upper gastro-intestinal bleeding.   True/False

c. Gallstones cause obstructive jaundice when stuck in Hartman's pouch.   True/False

d. The presence of jaundice should prompt a travel history.   True/False

e. The presence of jaundice should prompt an occupation history.   True/False

Mcqs for GPVTS

HAEMATOLOGY

103 The following is true regarding pernicious anaemia. **HAEM**

a. Patients have an increased risk of gastric carcinoma True/False

b. It is more common in blood group O. True/False

c. If folate also deficient, it should be replenished first before B12 is given. True/False

d. Hypokalaemia is common with treatment. True/False

e. Complete reversal of neurological signs is achievable with therapy. True/False

104 White cell counts. **HAEM**

a. Neutrophil counts below the normal range may be normal for Afro-caribbean patients. True/False

b. Neutrophils are decreased in haemorrhage. True/False

c. Eosinophils are decreased in asthma. True/False

d. Lymphocytes are decreased in viral illnesses. True/False

e. Neutrophil counts are increased by steroids. True/False

105	The following causes of anaemia are correctly matched with their morphological classification.	HAEM

a. Thalassaemia: Microcytic.   True/False

b. Pregnancy: Microcytic.   True/False

c. Renal failure: Macrocytic.   True/False

d. Alcohol: Macrocytic.   True/False

e. Folate deficiency: Normocytic.   True/False

106	Peripheral blood film.	HAEM

a. Leukoerythroblastic picture is suggestive of malignancy.   True/False

b. Schistocytes suggest a trematode infection such as schistosomiasis.   True/False

c. Dimorphic blood picture suggests two populations of red cells and signifies a clonal expansion (malignancy) of a cell line.   True/False

d. Hypochromia suggests poor staining technique and a need to repeat the test.   True/False

e. A leukaemoid reaction is a picture seen in early leukaemia.   True/False

107 The following are recognised causes of macrocytic anaemia.   **HAEM**

  a. Alcoholism.   True/False

  b. Haemolysis.   True/False

  c. Diabetes mellitus.   True/False

  d. Hypothyroidism.   True/False

  e. Pregnancy.   True/False

108 The following are useful tests in pernicious anaemia.   **HAEM**

  a. Mantoux test.   True/False

  b. Clo test.   True/False

  c. Schilling test.   True/False

  d. Anti-endomysial antibody.   True/False

  e. Anti-parietal cell antibody.   True/False

109 The following can lead to polycythaemia.   **HAEM**

a. Myeloproliferative disorder.   True/False

b. Mountain climbing.   True/False

c. Chronic bronchitis.   True/False

d. Small cell lung carcinoma.   True/False

e. Chronic renal failure.   True/False

110 The following is true regarding thalassaemia.   **HAEM**

a. Most prevalent amongst South Americans.   True/False

b. Iron overload from transfusions causes severe morbidity.   True/False

c. Post surgical deep vein thrombosis is more common.   True/False

d. Factor IX is deficient.   True/False

e. Splenectomy is a treatment option.   True/False

111 The following lead to a thrombocytopenia.　　　　**HAEM**

a. NSAIDs.　　　　　　　　　　　　　　　　　　True/False

b. Warfarin.　　　　　　　　　　　　　　　　　　True/False

c. Low molecular weight heparin.　　　　　　　　True/False

d. Clopidogrel.　　　　　　　　　　　　　　　　True/False

e. Splenectomy.　　　　　　　　　　　　　　　　True/False

112 Haemophilia.　　　　　　　　　　　　　　　　**HAEM**

a. Haemophilias are inherited diseases.　　　　　True/False

b. Christmas disease involves a deficiency of factor IX.　　True/False

c. Includes factor V leiden deficiency.　　　　　　True/False

d. Tends to cause minor mucosal bleeds.　　　　　True/False

e. Injections should be given intramuscularly (i.m.) rather than　True/False
intravenously to avoid haemorrhage at venepuncture sites.

113 The following disorders are correctly matched with their characteristic blood result.　**HAEM**

a. Disseminated intravascular coagulation: INR rises. 　True/False

b. Vitamin K deficiency: APTT rises. 　True/False

c. Christmas disease: PT rises. 　True/False

d. Warfarin therapy: APTT rises. 　True/False

e. Von Willebrand's disease: APTT rises. 　True/False

114 The following scenarios are correctly matched with the appropriate action in an anticoagulated patient. 　**HAEM**

a. INR > 6 and no bleeding: Stop warfarin and give low dose oral vitamin K. 　True/False

b. INR 9 and no bleeding: Stop warfarin and give intravenous vitamin K. 　True/False

c. INR > 5 and perforated viscus: Stop warfarin and give fresh frozen plasma or cryoprecipitate 　True/False

d. INR >10 and no bleeding: Stop warfarin and give fresh frozen plasma or cryoprecipitate 　True/False

e. INR 4-5 and no bleeding: Reduce warfarin dose or omit. 　True/False

115 Neutropenic sepsis.   HAEM

a. If temperature is 37.0 degrees or greater on two separate occasions at least one hour apart then antibiotics should be given.   True/False

b. A full examination including search for skin, ENT and anal lesions including a rectal examination (PR) should be undertaken to find a septic focus.   True/False

c. Vulnerability to infections may occur from the first day after chemotherapy.   True/False

d. Is less common nowadays due to routine use of granulocyte colony stimulating factor (GCSF).   True/False

e. Fungal infections are as important as bacterial and prophylaxis is commonly offered.   True/False

116 The following are features of poor prognosis in acute lymphoblastic leukaemia (ALL).   HAEM

a. Male sex.   True/False

b. Presentation in childhood.   True/False

c. Absence of CNS involvement.   True/False

d. Philadelphia chromosome (9:22 translocation).   True/False

e. Blood group AB.   True/False

117 Acute myeloid leukaemia (AML).	**HAEM**

a. Is diagnosed by presence of myeloid blast cells in the peripheral blood.   True/False

b. Large lymph nodes causing mass effects are a rare but noted phenomenon.   True/False

c. The Reed-Sternberg cell is a feature.   True/False

d. Carries a high risk of gout during treatment.   True/False

e. Bone marrow transplant (BMT) is a curative treatment.   True/False

118 The following are recognised results of steroid therapy.	**HAEM**

a. Skin hyperpigmentation.   True/False

b. Osteomalacia.   True/False

c. Cataracts.   True/False

d. Pancreatitis.   True/False

e. Renal stones.   True/False

119	The following are recognised features of thalassaemia.	HAEM

a. Splenomegaly.   True/False

b. Endocrine failure.   True/False

c. Frontal bossing of the cranium.   True/False

d. Thrombosis.   True/False

e. Cardiomyopathy.   True/False

120	Non-Hodgkin's lymphoma	HAEM

a. Bone marrow transplant is a valuable treatment tool.   True/False

b. Low grade tumours are potentially curable whereas only   True/False
    remission is possible with high grade disease.

c. Epstein Barr virus (EBV) is implicated in some types.   True/False

d. H. pylori is implicated in some types.   True/False

e. Cytomegalo virus (CMV) has been implicated with some   True/False
    types.

121 Chronic myeloid leukaemia (CML).   **HAEM**

a. Auer rods are seen in myeloid blast cells.   True/False

b. Molecular inhibition of a tyrosine kinase gene product shows   True/False
the best promise of success in current therapy.

c. Philadelphia chromosome confers a worse prognosis.   True/False

d. This is most common in the elderly.   True/False

e. Massive splenomegaly is a noted feature.   True/False

122 The following are features of myeloproliferative disorders.   **HAEM**

a. Deep vein thrombosis.   True/False

b. Increased risk of acute leukaemia.   True/False

c. Increased risk of lymphoma.   True/False

d. Bleeding tendency.   True/False

e. Hyposplenism.   True/False

123 The following are associated with multiple myeloma.　　**HAEM**

a. Oligoclonal bands in serum.　　True/False

b. Bence Jones protein (BJP) in serum.　　True/False

c. Osteoporosis.　　True/False

d. Extramedullary haematopoiesis with bone deformity.　　True/False

e. Punched out lesions on bone X-ray.　　True/False

124 The following are recognised complications of multiple myeloma.　　**HAEM**

a. Renal failure.　　True/False

b. Pathological fracture.　　True/False

c. Splenic rupture.　　True/False

d. Prinzmetal angina.　　True/False

e. Hypercalcaemia.　　True/False

Interview Skills Consulting

125	The following are associated with raised paraprotein in the blood.	HAEM

a. Haemolytic anaemia.   True/False

b. Pancytopenia.   True/False

c. Plasma cell tumour.   True/False

d. Chronic lymphocytic leukaemia.   True/False

e. Thymoma.   True/False

126	The following is true of amyloidosis.	HAEM

a. Can cause cardiomyopathy.   True/False

b. Is a consequence of haemodyalisis.   True/False

c. Can cause a peripheral neuropathy.   True/False

d. Is associated with raised serum angiotensin converting   True/False
   enzyme (ACE).

e. Negative birifringence in polarised light is a diagnostic test.   True/False

127 Post-splenectomy   **HAEM**

a. Patients have an increased risk of bleeding.   True/False

b. Patients have an increased risk of acquiring anaerobic infections.   True/False

c. Repeat Bacille Calmette-Guérin (BCG) is required.   True/False

d. Protection against encapsulated organisms deminishes.   True/False

e. Life long steroids are needed to reduce risk of infections.   True/False

128 The following are associated with thrombosis.   **HAEM**

a. Anticardiolipin antibody.   True/False

b. Protein S deficiency.   True/False

c. Protein C deficiency.   True/False

d. Lupus vulgaris.   True/False

e. Behçet's syndrome.   True/False

129	The following are recognised features of subacute combined degeneration of the cord.	HAEM
a.	Ataxic gait.	True/False
b.	Lightening pains down the limbs.	True/False
c.	Absent ankle jerks.	True/False
d.	Myotonic jerks.	True/False
e.	Burns on lower limbs.	True/False

130	Iron studies and other tests in microcytic anaemia.	HAEM
a.	Ferritin levels may be affected by acute illness independently of iron status.	True/False
b.	Total iron binding capacity can help distinguish iron deficiency anaemia from that of chronic disease.	True/False
c.	High levels of iron are deposited in the marrow in sideroblastic anaemia.	True/False
d.	Reticulocytes are a recognised finding on blood film.	True/False
e.	Upper and lower gastrointestinal endoscopy should be readily undertaken if no immediate other cause of microcytic anaemia is found.	True/False

131 Chronic lymphocytic leukaemia (CLL). **HAEM**

a. Is commonly found in older adults and the elderly. True/False

b. Is often diagnosed by chance discovery of abnormalities on routine full blood count. True/False

c. Thrombosis leading to stroke and cardiac diasease as a consequence of hypercoagulability is the most common cause of death. True/False

d. Best treatment option is intensive chemotherapy followed by bone marrow transplant (BMT). True/False

e. Will eventually transform to acute leukaemia. True/False

132 The following are recognised causes of haemolytic anaemia. **HAEM**

a. Mycoplasma pneumonia with cold antibody formation. True/False

b. Rheumatoid arthritis. True/False

c. Sickle cell anaemia. True/False

d. Thalassaemia. True/False

e. Malaria. True/False

133	The following are features noted in haemolysis.	HAEM

a. Raised haptoglobin.   True/False

b. Raised bilirubin.   True/False

c. Decreased reticulocytes.   True/False

d. Hypochromasia.   True/False

e. Myoglobinuria.   True/False

134	The following are recognised features of Hodgkin's lymphoma.	HAEM

a. Pruritis.   True/False

b. Splenomegaly.   True/False

c. Maculopapular rash.   True/False

d. Urticaria.   True/False

e. Pain is worse when consuming alcohol.   True/False

135 The following is true of sickle cell anaemia.   **HAEM**

a. It is a genetic disease caused by a trinucleotide repeat of   True/False
   glutamine and valine residues coding for haemoglobin.

b. Heterozygotes have no clinical features.   True/False

c. Life-long penicillin may be necessary.   True/False

d. Opiate analgesia should be avoided in acute crises.   True/False

e. Exchange transfusions are required in severe disease.   True/False

136 The following are recognised complications of sickle cell   **HAEM**
anaemia.

a. Gallstones   True/False

b. Hyposplenism.   True/False

c. Pneumococcal infection.   True/False

d. Priapism.   True/False

e. Peyronie's disease.   True/False

ISCMEDICAL
Interview Skills Consulting

Mcqs for GPVTS

INFECTIOUS DISEASES

137 Sexually transmitted infections (STIs)   **INF.DIS.**

a. Warts are the most common infection in those under 25 in the UK.   True/False

b. Bacterial vaginosis is a sexual infection and so partners require prompt tracing and treatment.   True/False

c. Free chlamydia tests are available to under 25s in many high street chemists.   True/False

d. Trichomonas vaginalis (TV) is a female commensal organism which occasionally requires treatment due to discomfort and itch.   True/False

e. Genital herpes may present with acute urinary retention.   True/False

138 The following are recognised cautions with antituberculous medications.   **INF.DIS.**

a. Ethambutol causes optic neuritis.   True/False

b. Pyrazinamide causes discolouration of urine.   True/False

c. Rifampicin reduces the effect of warfarin.   True/False

d. Ethambutol may cause hepatitis.   True/False

e. Isoniazid leads to neuropathy.   True/False

139 Syphilis.   **INF.DIS.**

a. Was once prevalent but is now a declining sexually   True/False
   transmitted infection in the UK.

b. Causes a painless genital ulcer in primary infection.   True/False

c. Secondary syphilis can occur up to two years after primary True/False
   exposure and can resemble a glandular fever syndrome
   along with many other systemic signs.

d. Treponemes are difficult to culture but serial blood cultures True/False
   are of use.

e. False positive non-treponemal serology occurs during   True/False
   pregnancy and autoimmune diseases.

140 Vaginal and urethral discharge.   **INF.DIS.**

a. The vast majority of discharge in females is due to a   True/False
   sexually transmitted infection.

b. The vast majority of urethritis in young men is due to a   True/False
   sexually transmitted infection.

c. Chlamydia typically gives discharge in men, less so in   True/False
   women.

d. Bacterial STIs can innoculate the pharynx and so a history of True/False
   oral sex is essential.

e. Gonorrhoea is the most common cause of discharge and   True/False
   urethritis in men.

141 The following are recognised side effects of anti-HIV medications.   **INF.DIS.**

a. Stevens Johnson Syndrome.   True/False

b. Nightmares.   True/False

c. Pancreatitis.   True/False

d. Renal stones.   True/False

e. Hypertriglyceridaemia.   True/False

142 HIV management principles.   **INF.DIS.**

a. Viral loads are measured routinely as an indicator of effectiveness of treatment.   True/False

b. Viral loads suggest whether a patient is likely to need prophylaxis for opportunistic infections.   True/False

c. Many patients are treated with just one or two drugs alone.   True/False

d. Monogamous couples who are both HIV seropositive should still engage in safe sex.   True/False

e. Post exposure prophylaxis for needlestick injuries and even sexual exposure should be available in A&E departments.   True/False

Interview Skills Consulting

143 HIV testing.　　　　　　　　　　　　　　　　**INF.DIS.**

a.　Rapid diagnostic tests enable detection of HIV within one　　True/False
　　month of acquisition of the virus.

b.　HIV testing should only be undertaken when access to　　True/False
　　specialist pre and post test counselling is available i.e GUM
　　clinics.

c.　A CD4 count of <200 cells/mm^3 is indicator of risk of　　True/False
　　acquisition of significant opportunistic infections leading to
　　AIDS and so prophylaxis will be required.

d.　Most patients found to be HIV positive will require prompt　　True/False
　　commencement of antiretroviral medications.

e.　Insurance companies ask applicants whether or not they　　True/False
　　have had an HIV test and this turns many away from taking
　　a test.

144 Human immunodeficiency virus (HIV).　　　　　　**INF.DIS.**

a.　Is currently more commonly acquired in the UK by　　True/False
　　homosexual men.

b.　Oral sex accounts for up to 5% of transmissions.　　True/False

c.　Infects only CD4+ve T cells.　　True/False

d.　Features of acute infection present in the first week after　　True/False
　　transmission.

e.　Medical management of an HIV positive mother can reduce　　True/False
　　mother to foetus transmission to around 1%.

ISCMEDICAL
Interview Skills Consulting

145	Hepatitis B	INF.DIS.

a. Vaccination can be given over 1 month or 6 months.   True/False

b. Vaccination is recommended for prison inmates.   True/False

c. Antibodies to 'e' antigen in chronic hepatitis suggest low level of infectivity.   True/False

d. The antibody to the 'surface antogen' indicates level of immunity and seroconversion.   True/False

e. Successful vaccination renders a patient core antibody positive.   True/False

146	The following bacterium or group of bacterium are correctly matched with their microscopy appearance.	INF.DIS.

a. Neisseria meningitidis : Gram negative rods   True/False

b. Staphylococci : Gram positive cocci in chains.   True/False

c. Escherichia coli : Gram negative rods.   True/False

d. Clostridium difficile : Gram negative rods.   True/False

e. Pseudomonas aeruginosa : Gram positive rods.   True/False

147 Tuberculosis (TB) management. **INF.DIS.**

a. Cultures may take up to 3 months to result. True/False

b. Patients tend to start on four drugs for two months then convert to two drugs for four months. True/False

c. Tuberculin test may be more readily available and reliable, especially in immunocompromised patients. True/False

d. Patients with open or suspected TB should be nursed in positive pressure rooms. True/False

e. Thiamine should be given throughout treatment. True/False

148 Tuberculosis (TB) has been identified in the following sites. **INF.DIS.**

a. Retina. True/False

b. Testes. True/False

c. Appendix. True/False

d. Pericardium. True/False

e. Kidney. True/False

ISCMEDICAL
Interview Skills Consulting

149 Schistosomiasis and other imported infections.   **INF.DIS.**

a. Schistosomiasis acquisition is confined to Africa and the Middle East.   True/False

b. Schistosomiasis tends to affect just the renal tract.   True/False

c. Schistosomiasis can be confirmed on rectal biopsy.   True/False

d. Giardia can mimic malabsorption syndromes and even lactose intolerance.   True/False

e. Dengue fever typically presents with maculopapular rash after 2 weeks from exposure.   True/False

150 Tuberculosis (TB)   **INF.DIS.**

a. Respiratory isolation in uncomplicated pulmonary TB continues for at least 1 month then reassessed depending on respiratory markers.   True/False

b. Most primary acquisition is asymptomatic.   True/False

c. Milliary TB is due to the mycobacterial innoculum being aerosolised and so widely dispersed foci are seen as tiny lesions throughout the lung.   True/False

d. TB is common in the immunosuppressed because they are more likely to pick up the infection and be unable to cope with it.   True/False

e. DOTS is a strategy to improve compliance by admitting a patient and observing medication is taken, or to prescribe on a week by week basis in the community.   True/False

151 Hepatitis transmission and treatment.   **INF.DIS.**

a. Hepatitis E has a significant mortality in pregnancy.   True/False

b. Hepatitis A has an effective vaccine with no need for   True/False
boosters.

c. Hepatitis C carries a significant risk of liver carcinoma.   True/False

d. Intravenous drug use is a significant route for hepatitis E   True/False
transmission.

e. Hepatitis C has no effective treatment.   True/False

152 Malaria diagnosis and treatment.   **INF.DIS.**

a. If suspected one should send blood immediately for malaria   True/False
culture or PCR analysis.

b. Chloroquine is the mainstay of treatment for non-falciparum   True/False
malaria.

c. Low platelet count is suggestive of malaria in a traveller   True/False
returning from an endemic area.

d. Prophylaxis is given with some agents for a week before   True/False
departure to ensure adequate drug levels upon arrival in
endemic areas.

e. Blood sugars must be monitored in case of hypoglycaemia.   True/False

153 Malaria   **INF.DIS.**

a. Plasmodium falciparum has an incubation period of up to two weeks hence the need to take prophylaxis for two weeks after leaving an endemic area.   True/False

b. Plasmodium vivax can cause splenic rupture.   True/False

c. Benign malarias may lie dormant for over a year.   True/False

d. Plasmodium malariae is the most severe type.   True/False

e. The disease is caught after being bitten by the tsetse fly.   True/False

154 Gastroenteritis.   **INF.DIS.**

a. Winter vomiting disease is due to a contagious bacterium which for some will require antibiotics.   True/False

b. Consumption of a contaminated source more than 24 hours before onset of symptoms is unlikely to be due to salmonella.   True/False

c. Profuse diarrhoea more than 6 stools a day or dehydration warrants antibiotic therapy.   True/False

d. Cholera typically gives bloody diarrhoea.   True/False

e. Shigella is a cause of dysentry.   True/False

155 Varicella-Zoster.	**INF.DIS.**

a. Vesicular fluid can be sent for viral culture. — True/False

b. Ramsay Hunt syndrome is the VIIIth nerve palsy associated with ear problems. — True/False

c. Multidermatomal distribution of zoster suggests immunosuppression. — True/False

d. Post-herpetic neuralgia is reduced if antivirals are given during the acute phase. — True/False

e. Neuralgia is well treated with moderate opiates. — True/False

156 Herpes simplex virus.	**INF.DIS.**

a. Is only found on the oral or genital mucosa. — True/False

b. Oral herpes can be reliably treated by antiviral creams. — True/False

c. The benefit of antiviral medications is limited only to those who commence medication whilst new vesicles are forming. — True/False

d. The highest risk to an unborn child is maternal primary acquisition in the last trimester of pregnancy. — True/False

e. Type 2 is associated with more frequent recurrences. — True/False

157 Glandular fever.   **INF.DIS.**

a. Is associated with cytomegalovirus.   True/False

b. A false positive Monospot® test is recognised with   True/False
pancreatic carcinoma.

c. Amoxycillin should be avoided.   True/False

d. The underlying virus is associated with some lymphomas.   True/False

e. Splenic rupture is a rare but recognised complication.   True/False

158 Influenza virus.   **INF.DIS.**

a. Vaccination is recommended for those with mitral stenosis.   True/False

b. Vaccination is contraindicated in the immunosuppressed   True/False
because it may produce the disease.

c. The new H5N1 variant is a concern since it is not treatable   True/False
by standard anti influenza drugs.

d. Influenza vaccines must be taken yearly since they only   True/False
confer protection against that year's variant of the virus.

e. Current 'flu' vaccines confer some protection against avian   True/False
'flu'.

159 Cytomegalovirus (CMV)   **INF.DIS.**

a. Is a rare cause of hepatitis.   True/False

b. Blood products are screened for CMV.   True/False

c. Causes ring enhancing lesions on CT of brain if reactivated   True/False
   in HIV patients.

d. No effective treatment exists for this virus.   True/False

e. Is asymptomatic in most individuals.   True/False

160 Toxoplasmosis   **INF.DIS.**

a. Dogs are the usual animal host.   True/False

b. Up to half of all adults are infected by the time they reach old   True/False
   age.

c. Causes ring enhancing lesions in the brain on CT.   True/False

d. Infection is limited to neurological tissues.   True/False

e. Infection can cause a febrile illness similar to glandular   True/False
   fever.

Mcqs for GPVTS

NEUROLOGY

161 Epilepsy   NEURO

a. All patients should see a neurologist soon after a first   True/False
   seizure.

b. Seizures brought on by flashing lights are a myth.   True/False

c. Partial seizures are those in which consciousness is not lost.   True/False

d. A normal CT scan is sufficient to exclude a structural lesion   True/False
   as an underlying cause.

e. Blood glucose is essential in assessing a fitting patient.   True/False

162 The following deficits are correctly matched with their nerve   NEURO
       lesion.

a. Wrist drop : Ulnar nerve.   True/False

b. Foot drop : Tibial nerve.   True/False

c. Lost of sensation to the sole of foot : Tibial nerve.   True/False

d. Wasting of hypothenar eminence with loss of sensation to   True/False
   the lateral side of the hand : Ulnar nerve.

e. Loss of flexor pollicis brevis and sensation loss over the   True/False
   thumb : Median nerve.

163 Causes of mononeuritis multiplex include:	NEURO
a. Vasculitis.	True/False
b. Multiple sclerosis.	True/False
c. Diabetes mellitus.	True/False
d. Neoplasia.	True/False
e. Amyloidosis.	True/False

164 The following localising signs are correctly matched with the corresponding site of brain damage.	NEURO
a. Inability to perform calculations : Frontal lobe.	True/False
b. Loss of 2-point discrimination : Parietal lobe.	True/False
c. Perseveration : Frontal lobe.	True/False
d. Slurred speech : Frontal lobe.	True/False
e. Hemiparesis : Parietal lobe.	True/False

165 Brain tumours.	**NEURO**

a. Surgical intervention for an intracerebral tumour is only helpful if the tumour is accessible.   True/False

b. The most common tumours are metastases from breast or lung cancers.   True/False

c. Glioblastoma multiforme has the best prognosis of primary brain tumours.   True/False

d. Chemotherapy has no role in primary brain tumours.   True/False

e. Cerebral radiation has severe complications and so is reserved for a minority of cases.   True/False

166 Multiple sclerosis (MS).	**NEURO**

a. Patients may complain of electric shock sensations across the body.   True/False

b. Patients tend to experience symptoms in more than one site from the onset e.g. visual disturbance and weakness.   True/False

c. Symptoms worsen in cold weather.   True/False

d. The disease is confined to the central nervous system and so damage to the spinal cord is unheard of.   True/False

e. Treatment of acute episodes involves high dose oral steroids.   True/False

167 The following are recognised features of multiple sclerosis.　**NEURO**

a. Depression.　True/False

b. Urinary retention.　True/False

c. Ataxia.　True/False

d. Tremor.　True/False

e. Foot drop.　True/False

168 The following are of use in the management of Alzheimer's disease.　**NEURO**

a. Ginseng extract.　True/False

b. Hormone replacement therapy (HRT).　True/False

c. Amphetamines.　True/False

d. NMDA antagonists.　True/False

e. Acetycholinesterase inhibitors.　True/False

---

169 Parkinsonism.   **NEURO**

a. Asymetrical onset is typical of Parkinson's disease (PD).   True/False

b. Drug treatment should be instigated once bradykinesia   True/False
becomes evident in PD, to slow the progression to complete
dependence.

c. Inability to turn in bed at night may be the first sign of PD.   True/False

d. Drug induced parkinsonism responds better to   True/False
antimuscarinics than conventional antiparkinson's drugs.

e. 'Cogwheel rigidity' is a combination of bradykinesia and   True/False
tremor.

---

170 The following are recognised causes of autonomic   **NEURO**
neuropathy.

a. Guillain-Barré syndrome.   True/False

b. Diabetes mellitus.   True/False

c. Amyloidosis.   True/False

d. Multiple system atrophy.   True/False

e. Myasthenia gravis.   True/False

171 Epilepsy is highly likely: **NEURO**

a. If a patient experiences at least one seizure in response to   True/False
   hypoglycaemia.

b. If more than one muscle group is involved in abnormal motor   True/False
   activity.

c. If urinary incontinence is a feature of an episode.   True/False

d. If a patient experiences loss of consciousness.   True/False

e. If the patient bites the side of his/her tongue in repeated   True/False
   attacks.

172 Dementia.   **NEURO**

a. About a quarter of all dementia is due to vascular causes.   True/False

b. Lewy body dementia tends to give a step-wise progression   True/False
   in deficit.

c. Personality change may be one of the first features to   True/False
   present.

d. Fronto-temporal dementia leads to extrapyramidal signs   True/False
   along with dementia.

e. Pick's disease involves changes in personality with   True/False
   disinhibition.

173	The following have been shown to be associated with increased risk of developing Alzheimer's dementia.	NEURO

a. Cerebro-vascular disease.   True/False

b. Systemic lupus erythromatosis.   True/False

c. Downs' syndrome.   True/False

d. Temporal lobe epilepsy.   True/False

e. HIV.   True/False

174	Neuroimaging - Computerised Tomography (CT) vs Magnetic Resonance Imaging (MRI)	NEURO

a. MRI is better for imaging the posterior fossae than CT.   True/False

b. CT is invaluable in the assessment of multiple sclerosis (MS).   True/False

c. Subdural haematomas may be easily missed on CT.   True/False

d. MRI is superior to CT since it can accurately distinguish   True/False
   between abcess and tumour.

e. CT works by producing a composit of X-ray images.   True/False

175	The following are associated with poorer prognosis in patients with multiple sclerosis (MS).	NEURO

a. Black African origin.   True/False

b. Male sex.   True/False

c. Predominantly sensory symptoms.   True/False

d. Younger age.   True/False

e. Multiple lesions found on imaging.   True/False

176	The following are recognised causes of carpal tunnel syndrome.	NEURO

a. Acromegaly.   True/False

b. Osteitis fibrosis cystica.   True/False

c. Pregnancy.   True/False

d. Rheumatoid arthritis.   True/False

e. Amyloidosis.   True/False

---

177 Bell's palsy.   NEURO

a. If bilateral, may in fact be caused by Lyme disease.   True/False

b. Pain near the ear is a common feature.   True/False

c. If presenting after the third day of onset, treatment is not effective.   True/False

d. Is thought to be caused by CMV.   True/False

e. Surgery is indicated in those with a severe palsy.   True/False

---

178 Causes of seventh nerve palsy include: NEURO

a. Meningitis.   True/False

b. Otitis media.   True/False

c. Parotid tumour.   True/False

d. Sagittal sinus thrombosis.   True/False

e. Cavernous sinus thrombosis.   True/False

179 The following are recognised causes of polyneuropathies. **NEURO**

a. Wilson's disease. True/False

b. Chronic renal failure. True/False

c. Porphyria. True/False

d. Myasthenia gravis. True/False

e. Heavy metal poisoning. True/False

180 Guillain-Barré Syndrome. **NEURO**

a. Is a purely motor polyneuropathy. True/False

b. A poor prognosis is recognised when campylobacter is a precipitant. True/False

c. Diagnosis is unlikely if symptoms and signs commence proximally in limbs rather than distally followed by ascent. True/False

d. Is a demyelinating neuropathy. True/False

e. Cerebrospinal fluid protein is typically elevated. True/False

181 Dysarthria. **NEURO**

a. Is an inability to find words. True/False

b. May result from facial trauma. True/False

c. If the tongue is flaccid, motor neurone disease is likely. True/False

d. If the tongue is retracted and hypertonic, this is likely to be a pseudobulbar palsy. True/False

e. Stuttering speech suggests a cerebellar cause. True/False

182 Motor neurone disease (MND). **NEURO**

a. Diplopia occurs in a minority of patients. True/False

b. In late stages, the disease leads to paraesthesia, which disturbs patients at night. True/False

c. Diagnosis is aided by the presence of stimulating antibodies to acetycholine receptors. True/False

d. Bulbar features at onset confer the best prognosis. True/False

e. Although supportive management, with ventilation and nutrition has a role, no drug has been shown to improve outcome. True/False

183 The following is true of radiculopathy.　　　　　**NEURO**

a. Pain is invariably a complaint.　　　　　　　　　True/False

b. Symptoms may be worsened by movement.　　　　True/False

c. The muscles supplied by nerves involved will become　　True/False
hypertonic.

d. Reflexes will be diminished.　　　　　　　　　True/False

e. Disease at multiple sites is rare.　　　　　　　　True/False

184 The following are recognised features of myotonic dystrophy.　**NEURO**

a. Diabetes mellitus.　　　　　　　　　　　　　True/False

b. Cataracts.　　　　　　　　　　　　　　　　True/False

c. Drooling.　　　　　　　　　　　　　　　　True/False

d. Dementia.　　　　　　　　　　　　　　　　True/False

e. Hypothyroidism.　　　　　　　　　　　　　　True/False

185 The following are associated with myopathy. **NEURO**

a. Amyotrophic lateral sclerosis (ALS). True/False

b. Cushing's disease. True/False

c. Poliomyelitis. True/False

d. Statins. True/False

e. Chemotherapy. True/False

186 The following are known to exacerbate features in myasthenia gravis. **NEURO**

a. Pregnancy. True/False

b. Hyperkalaemia. True/False

c. NSAIDs. True/False

d. Antimalarials. True/False

e. Penicillins. True/False

187 The following are used in the diagnosis and management of myaesthenia gravis. **NEURO**

a. Anti tumour necrosis factor (TNF) alpha. True/False

b. Alpha blockade pre-thymic surgery. True/False

c. Plasmapheresis. True/False

d. Thymectomy. True/False

e. Nerve conduction studies. True/False

188 The following are true of neurofibromatosis. **NEURO**

a. Follows an autosomal dominant pattern of inheritance which demonstrates anticipation. True/False

b. Café au lait patches can develop into melanomas. True/False

c. The number of neurofibromas suggest which subtype of the disease is present (1 or 2). True/False

d. Is associated with acoustic neuromas. True/False

e. Is associated with phaeochromocytomas. True/False

189 The following are recognised causes of dementia. **NEURO**

a. Wilson's disease.   True/False

b. HIV.   True/False

c. Pork tape worm.   True/False

d. Hypothyroidism.   True/False

e. Parkinson's disease.   True/False

190 The following are associations of Myasthenia Gravis. **NEURO**

a. Pernicious anaemia.   True/False

b. Prolactinoma.   True/False

c. Psoriasis.   True/False

d. Pyoderma gangrenosum.   True/False

e. Vitiligo.   True/False

191 The following are recognised to increase risk of stroke.   **NEURO**

a. Multiple myeloma.   True/False

b. Hypotension.   True/False

c. Alcohol excess.   True/False

d. Migraine.   True/False

e. Polycythaemia rubra vera.   True/False

192 The following are recognised features of syringomyelia.   **NEURO**

a. Weakness and wasting of the hands.   True/False

b. Horner's syndrome.   True/False

c. Isolated mononeuropathies.   True/False

d. 'Cape-like' sensory deficit.   True/False

e. Multiple burns and minor traumas in the limbs.   True/False

193 The middle cerebral artery. NEURO

a. Is part of the vertebral artery system. True/False

b. Infarction leads to ipsilateral arm weakness. True/False

c. Infarction leads to contralateral leg weakness. True/False

d. Infarction leads to contralateral homonymous hemianopia. True/False

e. Infarction can lead to apraxia (difficulty performing multicomponent tasks). True/False

194 Headache. NEURO

a. Cluster headaches tend to respond to simple analgesia if treated soon after symptoms present. True/False

b. Early morning headache is associated with obstructive sleep apnoea (OSA). True/False

c. Can be made worse or persist with codeine and other opiates. True/False

d. With eye watering suggests sinusitis. True/False

e. Trigeminal neuralgia gives headache and facial pain due to jaw claudication while eating. True/False

195	Migraine.	**NEURO**

a. With aura, is a contraindication for the combined oral contraceptive pill.   True/False

b. If one looks hard enough, a trigger is identified in about three quarters of patients.   True/False

c. Visual aura is usually unilateral.   True/False

d. Aura can affect the speech and coordination.   True/False

e. Is more common in women than men.   True/False

196	Blackouts	**NEURO**

a. In a vasovagal attack, there is no amnesia of the event.   True/False

b. Drop attacks have sudden onset with loss of consciousness that last for no more than 2 minutes.   True/False

c. Stokes-Adams attacks are due to a decreased cardiac output leading to loss of consciousness and so will only occur on standing.   True/False

d. Urinary incontinence is pathognomic of epilepsy.   True/False

e. Unsteadiness on standing from a sitting or lying position can point to Addison's disease.   True/False

197 Vertigo — **NEURO**

a. Is common in those with a fear of heights. True/False

b. Is almost always associated with hearing loss or tinitus. True/False

c. Is a feature of Ramsay Hunt syndrome. True/False

d. Can be caused by gentamicin. True/False

e. Is associated with otosclerosis. True/False

198 The following are known to be associated with vertigo. — **NEURO**

a. Carotid sinus hypersensitivity. True/False

b. Migraine. True/False

c. Epilepsy. True/False

d. Travel sickness. True/False

e. Acoustic neuroma. True/False

199	Spinal cord compression	NEURO

a. Is most commonly caused by trauma or sepsis.   True/False

b. Urgent treatment with high dose intravenous steroids will limit irreversible damage in many.   True/False

c. Motor paralysis is solely upper motor neurone in type.   True/False

d. If sensory loss is found up to the level of the thighs, then imaging from the lumbar region downwards is indicated.   True/False

e. Will present with flaccid paralysis in the preliminary stages.   True/False

200	The following are common causes of absent ankle jerks with extensor plantar responses.	NEURO

a. Freidrich's ataxia.   True/False

b. Wilson's disease.   True/False

c. B12 deficiency.   True/False

d. Myasthenia gravis.   True/False

e. Diabetes mellitus.   True/False

201 The following can lead to bladder and bowel disturbance. **NEURO**

a. Diabetes mellitus.   True/False

b. Lesion to the cauda equina.   True/False

c. Syringomyelia.   True/False

d. Guillain-Barré syndrome.   True/False

e. Transverse myelitis.   True/False

202 Recognised causes of spastic paraparesis include: **NEURO**

a. Trauma to lower lumbar vertabrae.   True/False

b. B12 deficiency.   True/False

c. Tabes dorsalis.   True/False

d. Diabetes mellitus.   True/False

e. Multiple sclerosis.   True/False

203	Movement disorders.	NEURO

a. If a patient concentrates, they can suppress tics.   True/False

b. Myoclonus is involuntary jerking at rest.   True/False

c. Chorea is confluent involuntary movements in any limb of the body.   True/False

d. Athetosis is continuous grouped movements more coarse than chorea.   True/False

e. Hemibalismus often affects proximal muscles.   True/False

204	Delirium.	NEURO

a. Can present with paranoid delusions.   True/False

b. Manifests after a day of alcohol withdrawal in an alcoholic.   True/False

c. May be associated with poverty of speech and withdrawal.   True/False

d. May be due to status epilepticus.   True/False

e. Hallucinations tend to be visual and auditory in nature.   True/False

205	Strokes	NEURO

a. Purely motor or pure sensory strokes are rare.   True/False

b. Acute hypertension in stroke must be controlled to prevent   True/False
   further damage due to intracerebral haemorrhage and
   oedema.

c. In a young person, strokes are unlikely to be due to   True/False
   thromboembolism.

d. Nominal aphasia suggests a frontal lesion.   True/False

e. Any stroke is an absolute contraindication for thrombolysis in   True/False
   the event of an MI in later life.

206	The following are associated with subarachnoid haemorrhage (SAH).	NEURO

a. Polycystic kidney disease.   True/False

b. Marfan's syndrome.   True/False

c. Seropositive rheumatoid arthritis.   True/False

d. Osteogenesis imperfecta.   True/False

e. Sickle cell anaemia.   True/False

207 Meningitis. **NEURO**

a. Listeria monocytogenes tends to affect just the elderly and   True/False
   neonates, but can also affect the immunosuppressed
   especially if eating unpasteurised foods.

b. Unless known allergy to penicillin, i.m. benzylpenicillin must   True/False
   be given to those in community in whom bacterial meningitis
   is suspected.

c. Septicaemic meningitis has a worse prognosis than   True/False
   prodominantly meningitic type.

d. Tuberculous meningitis treatment commences with the same   True/False
   drugs as that for pulmonary tuberculosis.

e. Lumbar puncture is futile once antibiotics have been   True/False
   administered.

208 The following are associated with abacterial meningitis. **NEURO**

a. Behçet's disease   True/False

b. Reiters disease   True/False

c. NSAIDs   True/False

d. Scleroderma   True/False

e. Leukaemia   True/False

209 The following are recognised risk factors for bacterial meningitis.   **NEURO**

a. Pneumonia   True/False

b. Sinusitis   True/False

c. Pregnancy   True/False

d. Cystic fibrosis   True/False

e. Haemochromatosis   True/False

210 Cerebrospinal fluid (CSF) in meningitis.   **NEURO**

a. Is clear in viral meningitis.   True/False

b. PCR is helpful to diagnose viral meningitis.   True/False

c. Gram stain will show organisms in bacterial and TB meningitis.   True/False

d. India ink stain is positive in toxoplasmosis.   True/False

e. High lymphocytes and low polymorphonucleocytes (PMNs) count makes bacterial meningitis unlikely.   True/False

211 Extradural haematoma.   **NEURO**

a. Raised blood pressure and bradycardia (Cushing's reflex)   True/False
   are early warning signs of raised intracranial pressure in this
   condition.

b. A biconcave lesion of trapped blood is a classical CT finding. True/False

c. The typical history is of head injury followed by decreased   True/False
   level of consciousness which gradually deteriorates.

d. The cause is by a venous and/or arterial bleed.   True/False

e. Skull x-ray often shows evidence of trauma and/or bleeding.   True/False

212 Subdural haematoma.   **NEURO**

a. Are more common in elderly than younger patients.   True/False

b. Surgery can lead to complete recovery.   True/False

c. Typical appearances are of a 'crescent' shaped peripheral   True/False
   density.

d. Gradual changes in intracranial pressure can cause   True/False
   fluctuations in level of consciousness.

e. The cause is a venous tear.   True/False

| 213 | Which of the following gait abnormalities are typical of their matched conditions? | NEURO |

a. Excessive hesitation to move with improvement when distracted : Parkinsonism.   True/False

b. Increase lateral leg swing and 'leg scissoring' : Spastic.   True/False

c. Cannot walk along a straight line without falling : Apraxia.   True/False

d. Foot slapping or stamping gait : Dorsal column damage.   True/False

e. Waddling gait : proximal myopathy.   True/False

| 214 | Subarachnoid haemorrhage (SAH). | NEURO |

a. A sudden headache like a thunderclap is diagnostic of SAH   True/False

b. Berry aneurysms confer a risk of SAH and any detected should be surgically treated.   True/False

c. Stool softeners form part of management for SAH.   True/False

d. Lumbar puncture is best after 12 hours of symptoms.   True/False

e. Gaze palsies are helpful to indicate site of bleed.   True/False

215 The following are of value in a stroke patient.   **NEURO**

a. Hepatitis serology.   True/False

b. VDRL.   True/False

c. Erythrocyte sedimentation rate.   True/False

d. Packed cell volume.   True/False

e. Plasma osmolality.   True/False

216 Transient ischaemic attacks (TIAs).   **NEURO**

a. Absence of carotid bruits makes carotid atherosclerosis an   True/False
    unlikely cause.

b. By definition, symptoms resolve within 12 hours of onset.   True/False

c. Carotid endarterectomy is indicated if stenosis is greater   True/False
    than 50%.

d. Smoking cessation is less effective at reducing stroke risk   True/False
    than in preventing myocardial infarction.

e. Migraine is a differential diagnosis.   True/False

217 Stroke management.   **NEURO**

a. Prompt surgery is an option.   True/False

b. Aspirin in the immediate stage is indicated in ischaemic   True/False
   strokes.

c. For those with AF or heart valve disease, warfarin should be   True/False
   started within the first few days.

d. Dedicated stroke units have been proven to confer reduced   True/False
   morbidity but not reduced mortality.

e. All patients should undergo CT or MRI.   True/False

218 Thromboembolism and stroke.   **NEURO**

a. Deep venous thromboses (DVTs) lead to strokes.   True/False

b. All replaced heart valves require anticoagulation to an INR of   True/False
   between 3.5 and 4.5.

c. Stroke risk with atrial fibrillation is further reduced by adding True/False
   aspirin to warfarin.

d. Almost all thromboembolic insults on the brain will produce   True/False
   clinical features even if short lived.

e. Benefits of thrombolysis have been shown to outweigh risks   True/False
   if given up to but no later than 12 hours from the onset of a
   proven ischaemic event.

MCQs for GPVTS

ONCOLOGY

219 Radiotherapy. **ONCOL**

a. Is hardly ever given during the same time period as a course of chemotherapy. True/False

b. The term 'fraction' refers to the fraction of radiation dose given at each session. True/False

c. Nausea is a common side effect. True/False

d. Interstitial pneumonitis is an early side effect of treatment. True/False

e. Topical creams to treat burns are used during treatment sessions. True/False

220 The following are recognised features of superior vena cava obstruction. **ONCOL**

a. Facial palor. True/False

b. Seizures. True/False

c. Haemoptysis. True/False

d. Dyspnoea. True/False

e. Dysphagia. True/False

221	BRCA.	**ONCOL**

a. Is a tumour marker for breast carcinoma.   True/False

b. It is associated with pancreatic carcinoma.   True/False

c. Those with BRCA may be offered prophylactic bilateral   True/False
salpingoopherectomy.

d. It is found in over 50% of cases of breast carcinoma.   True/False

e. Males with BRCA2 are at increased risk of developing breast   True/False
carcinoma.

222	HNPCC (hereditary non-polyposis colorectal cancer).	**ONCOL**

a. Surveillance with regular sigmoidoscopy is required.   True/False

b. Patients are at increased risk of gyneacological and urinary   True/False
tract carcinomas.

c. Prophylactic colectomy is advised in many before they reach   True/False
50 years of age.

d. Personal risk of developing a tumour is related to the degree   True/False
of relationship to any family members affected.

e. The defect is related to the APC gene.   True/False

223	The following treatments are beneficial in Superior Vena Cava obstruction.	ONCOL

a. Intravenous steroids. — True/False

b. Radiotherapy. — True/False

c. Chemotherapy. — True/False

d. Stenting. — True/False

e. Anticoagulation. — True/False

224	Oncology terminology.	ONCOL

a. Brachytherapy : Small doses of radiotherapy given over a prolonged period of time. — True/False

b. Debulking surgery : Any surgery for solid organ cancers where a mass is removed. — True/False

c. Intrathecal chemotherapy : Where cytotoxics are injected into a tumour. — True/False

d. Adjuvant therapy : Therapy given in addition to complete tumour excision to reduce the chance of recurrence. — True/False

e. Neoadjuvant therapy : Newer non-cytotoxic e.g. hormonal drugs given in addition to tumour excision. — True/False

Interview Skills Consulting

| 225 | Palliation in oncology. | ONCOL |

a. Benzodiazepines are contraindicated if patient is short of   True/False
    breath.

b. Hand held fans can reduce dyspnoea.   True/False

c. Oxycodone is a more potent alternative to morphine.   True/False

d. Palliative care teams should not be involved unless a case   True/False
    has been deemed incurable or has entered the terminal
    phase.

e. Nerve blocks are used to treat intractable pain.   True/False

MCQs for GPVTS

PHARMACOLOGY

226 | Cardiac medications | **PHARM**

a. Aspirin is a COX inhibitor. | True/False

b. Clopidogrel reduces platelet aggregation by interaction with von Willebrand factor | True/False

c. Beta blockers are negatively inotropic and negatively chronotropic. | True/False

d. Statins are HMG CoA reductase inhibitors causing a decline in macrophage cholesterol production. | True/False

e. Digoxin acts on the sodium/potassium pump having an inotropic effect. | True/False

---

227 | Management of Asthma | **PHARM**

a. Prednisolone courses are only to be used if inhaled steroids have been tried and failed. | True/False

b. Move to step two only if inhaled beta agonists in step one are used 3 or more times a day. | True/False

c. Step three involves changing to a long acting beta agonist or leukotriene inhibitor. | True/False

d. Step four includes considering ipratropium bromide preparations. | True/False

e. Sodium Chromoglycate does not feature in the British Thoracic Society (BTS) step guidelines. | True/False

228 Amfebutamone. **PHARM**

a. Can increase smoking quit rate by 80% at 1year.   True/False

b. Is the first line choice of drug to aid smoking cessation.   True/False

c. Can cause seizures.   True/False

d. Is contraindicated in pregnancy.   True/False

e. Will interact with antimalarials.   True/False

229 Drugs and renal impairment. **PHARM**

a. Dosing of low molecular weight heparins needs to be increased.   True/False

b. Penicillins and cephalosporins are contraindicated.   True/False

c. Digoxin dose needs to be reduced.   True/False

d. Warfarin dose needs to be reduced.   True/False

e. Statins are contraindicated.   True/False

---

230 The following drugs should be avoided in liver failure.	**PHARM**

a. Oxycodone. — True/False

b. Mycrogynon ®. — True/False

c. Lactulose. — True/False

d. Aspirin. — True/False

e. Glipizide. — True/False

---

231 Regarding ACE inhibitors.	**PHARM**

a. Are the drug of choice in hypertension of pregnancy. — True/False

b. Dose has to be reduced in aortic stenosis. — True/False

c. Side-effects can be reduced if taken before bed time. — True/False

d. Dry cough is noticed in about 10% of patients. — True/False

e. Are contraindicated in diabetic nephropathy disease. — True/False

232 Medications and rheumatoid arthritis **PHARM**

a. Naproxen is a disease modifying agent. True/False

b. Folic acid must be given in conjunction with methotrexate. True/False

c. Daily methotrexate may be required in up to a quarter of patients. True/False

d. Azathioprine is associated with gum hypertrophy. True/False

e. Sulphasalazine causes oligospermia. True/False

233 Digoxin. **PHARM**

a. Acts on the sodium/calcium/potassium pump. True/False

b. Is contraindicated in HOCM. True/False

c. May lead to a tachycardia or a bradycardia. True/False

d. Toxicity can be enhanced in hypokalaemia. True/False

e. Has been proven to improve mortality in heart failure. True/False

234 Anticonvulsants.   **PHARM**

a. Management should commence with just one drug.   True/False

b. Valproate leads to blood dyscrasias.   True/False

c. Phenytoin can lead to acne.   True/False

d. Phenytoin will decrease the effects of warfarin.   True/False

e. Lamotrigine is becoming first line drug of choice for generalised seizures.   True/False

235 Parkinson's medications   **PHARM**

a. Common formulations of levadopa also include a peripheral dopa decarboxylase inhibitor.   True/False

b. Pergolide is a dopamine agonist.   True/False

c. Entacapone is a dopamine agonist.   True/False

d. Anticholinergics are added to some patient's regimens.   True/False

e. Apomorphine can be given as an infusion and is of use when patients are undergoing surgery.   True/False

---

236 Cardiac medications   **PHARM**

a. Calcium channel blockers such as nifedipine dilate peripheral vessels and slow AV conduction in dysrhythmias.   True/False

b. Verapamil is contraindicated with carvedilol.   True/False

c. Diltiazem is contraindicated in heart block.   True/False

d. Metolozone is a loop diuretic used in advanced congestive heart failure.   True/False

e. Ankle swelling is a common side effect of calcium channel blockers.   True/False

---

237 Management of type 2 diabetes.   **PHARM**

a. The most important aspect of managing patients with type 2 diabetes is strict glycaemic control.   True/False

b. Acarbose can lead to bloating and abdominal pains.   True/False

c. Rhabdomyolysis is a well recognised side effect of metformin.   True/False

d. Repaglinide inhibits starch breakdown in the gut.   True/False

e. Glitazones should not be taken with metformin.   True/False

---

238 The following are absolute contraindications to sildenafil use.　**PHARM**

a. Active peptic ulceration.　　　　　　　　　　　True/False

b. Warfarin.　　　　　　　　　　　　　　　　　　True/False

c. Prostate cancer.　　　　　　　　　　　　　　　True/False

d. Peyronie's disease.　　　　　　　　　　　　　　True/False

e. NYHA grade one heart failure.　　　　　　　　　True/False

---

239 Laxatives.　　　　　　　　　　　　　　　　　　**PHARM**

a. Stimulant laxatives such as lactulose increase intestinal　True/False
motility.

b. Sodium ducusate has a stimulant and softening effect.　True/False

c. Lactulose may be effective in managing hepatic　　　True/False
encephalopathy.

d. Ispaghula husk is an osmotic agent leading to retention of　True/False
fluid in the bowel lumen and aiding stool passage.

e. Fybogel® is a bulking agent.　　　　　　　　　　True/False

240 Side effects of sildenafil include the following. **PHARM**

a. Tremor. True/False

b. Dyspepsia. True/False

c. Nasal congestion. True/False

d. Headache. True/False

e. Distortion of colour vision. True/False

241 Treatment of Diabetes Mellitus. **PHARM**

a. Glargine is a long acting insulin reserved only for use in type 2 diabetes. True/False

b. Insulatard is a long acting insulin. True/False

c. Porcine insuline is now banned in the UK. True/False

d. Novorapid is a much faster acting insulin than actrapid. True/False

e. Insulin can only be delivered via a subcutaneous needle. True/False

MCQs for GPVTS

RENAL MEDICINE

242 Rheumatology and the Kidney. **RENAL**

a. Penicillamine can lead to glomerulonephritis. True/False

b. SLE rarely affects the kidney. True/False

c. Amyloidosis occurs in up to 15% of rheumatoid patients. True/False

d. Renal disease in seronegative arthropathy is mainly secondary to medications. True/False

e. Renal transplant is contraindicated in those with CREST syndrome. True/False

243 Acute renal failure. **RENAL**

a. Is unlikely with a creatinine of <125 mcmol/l. True/False

b. An ECG is essential. True/False

c. Oedema should only be treated by diuretics. True/False

d. Nitrate infusions are useful for pulmonary oedema. True/False

e. Myocarditis is a noted complication. True/False

244 The following give false positive for 'blood' on urine dipstick. **RENAL**

  a. Rhabdomyolysis.   True/False

  b. Rifampacin.   True/False

  c. Porphyria.   True/False

  d. Haemochromatosis.   True/False

  e. Pseudopseudohypoparathyroidism.   True/False

245 Haematuria.   **RENAL**

  a. If macroscopic, should be referred to a nephrologist when it   True/False
      persists more than a week.

  b. If microscopic and with no hypertension nor proteinuria,   True/False
      makes nephritis syndrome unlikely.

  c. An episode of haematospermia should be promptly referred   True/False
      to a urologist.

  d. Is uncommon in adult polycystic kidney disease.   True/False

  e. If oedema is present, this suggests nephrotic syndrome.   True/False

246 Urine analysis.   **RENAL**

a. Crystals signify an excess of excreted materials and hence a   True/False
   metabolic or glomerular disease.

b. Red cell casts suggest bladder pathology.   True/False

c. Hyaline casts suggest membrane disease, a subset of   True/False
   glomerulonephritis.

d. Bence Jones protein suggests plasma cell neoplasia.   True/False

e. Protein is raised post ejaculation.   True/False

247 Abdominal x-ray in nephrology.   **RENAL**

a. Can rule out about 90% of calculi.   True/False

b. Will reveal abnormalities in acute tubular necrosis.   True/False

c. Diabetes mellitus is a relative contraindication to contrast   True/False
   enhancement.

d. Sickle cell anaemia is a relative contraindication to contrast   True/False
   enhancement.

e. Is the first line imaging modality if uncomplicated   True/False
   nephrolithiasis suspected.

---

248 Renal biopsy.   **RENAL**

a. Is reserved for chronic renal failure or ensuing glomerular disease.   True/False

b. Is contraindicated in transplanted kidneys where it may induce recurrence of primary disease.   True/False

c. Retroperitoneal haematoma and sepsis are the main complications.   True/False

d. Is undertaken with the aid of CT guidance.   True/False

e. Is undertaken with patient lying prone.   True/False

---

249 Renal imaging.   **RENAL**

a. Ultrasound scanning is the investigation of choice if hydronephrosis is suspected.   True/False

b. Kidneys tend to be large if chronic inflammation is present.   True/False

c. Retrograde pyelography is contraindicated in those who cannot tolerate intravenous contrast media.   True/False

d. Radionucleotide imaging is required for an accurate assessment of glomerular filtration rate.   True/False

e. Ultrasound can rule out tumours of the renal pelvis.   True/False

250 Urinary tract infection.   **RENAL**

a. E.coli is the most common cause.   True/False

b. To appropriately test for TB, three early morning samples are required.   True/False

c. The diaphragm contraceptive device is a risk factor.   True/False

d. Ciprofloxacin is the treatment of choice in pregnancy.   True/False

e. Randomised control trial evidence has shown that cranberry juice can reduce bacteruria.   True/False

---

251 Nephrolithiasis.   **RENAL**

a. Calcium oxalate stones show on X-ray.   True/False

b. Almost all stones lead to renal colic.   True/False

c. Ureteric stones <5mm will pass spontaneously.   True/False

d. Low calcium intake is advised with calcium stones.   True/False

e. May be a sign of underlying neoplasia.   True/False

252 Renal tract obstruction.   **RENAL**

a. Absence of a palpable bladder makes urinary tract   True/False
   obstruction unlikely.

b. Recurrent urinary tract obstruction is a feature of ovarian   True/False
   carcinoma.

c. Lithotripsy of staghorn calculi can be complicated by   True/False
   obstruction.

d. Is associated with antimigraine remedies.   True/False

e. Is a recognised feature of seronegative arthropathies.   True/False

253 Glomerulonephritis.   **RENAL**

a. Membranous is associated with underlying malignancy.   True/False

b. Minimal change is overall the most common type.   True/False

c. Less than 5% of Henoch-Schönlein purpura will deteriorate   True/False
   to renal failure.

d. Up to 50% of focal segmental glomerulosclerosis leads to   True/False
   end stage renal failure.

e. Rapidly progressive glomerulonephrosis responds poorly to   True/False
   steroids.

254 Diabetes insipidis (DI)   **RENAL**

a. Is due to a dysfunction in the ADH-renal axis.   True/False

b. Nephrogenic is related to an insensitivity of the kidney to   True/False
    vasopressin.

c. Cranial DI is a 'functional' condition.   True/False

d. The water deprivation test is a method of confirming the   True/False
    diagnosis.

e. Diuretic therapy will interfere with tests for DI.   True/False

255 Recognised complications of nephrotic syndrome include: **RENAL**

a. Hyperlipidaemia.   True/False

b. Thromboembolism.   True/False

c. Blurred vision.   True/False

d. Acute renal failure.   True/False

e. Tremors.   True/False

256	The following diseases are characterised by renal involvement.	RENAL

a. Alpha 1 antitrypsin deficiency.   True/False

b. Tuberous sclerosis.   True/False

c. Systemic sclerosis.   True/False

d. Behçet's disease.   True/False

e. Wilson's disease.   True/False

257	Common causes of chronic renal failure include:	RENAL

a. Hypertension.   True/False

b. Glomerulonephritis.   True/False

c. Multiple myeloma.   True/False

d. Nephrolithiasis.   True/False

e. Analgesic nephropathy.   True/False

258 Chronic renal failure.   **RENAL**

a. Kidneys are usually small on ultrasound.   True/False

b. Angiotensin converting enzyme inhibitors (ACEi) are contraindicated.   True/False

c. Lipid related cardiovascular risks are significantly higher than those with normal renal function.   True/False

d. All patients should have potassium restriction.   True/False

e. Iron deficiency anaemia is common.   True/False

259 Complications of dialysis include: **RENAL**

a. Carpal tunnel syndrome.   True/False

b. Malabsorption.   True/False

c. Ischaemic heart disease.   True/False

d. Anterior uveitis.   True/False

e. Tendency to bleeding of mucus membranes.   True/False

260 Dialysis.

a. Peritoneal dialysis is contraindicated in the elderly. True/False

b. Continuous ambulatory peritoneal dialysis involves between 3 and 5 bag changes a day. True/False

c. Uraemic pericarditis is an indication for acute dialysis. True/False

d. Can be performed via a peripheral venous line if in an emergency. True/False

e. Peritoneal dialysis can cause decompensation of abdominal hernias. True/False

MCQs for GPVTS

RESPIRATORY MEDICINE

261 Regarding the chest x-ray.   **RESP**

a. PA films enlarge the heart border.   True/False

b. The sail sign visible through the heart suggests left lower
    lobe collapse.   True/False

c. Wegeners granulomatosis can causes reticular, nodular and
    consolidative changes.   True/False

d. Air bronchogram suggests alveolar consolidation.   True/False

e. Consolidation leads to mediastinal shift.   True/False

262 Asthma.   **RESP**

a. Is characterised as a reversible airways obstruction and
    hyper-responsiveness.   True/False

b. Critical airways obstruction can characteristically occur with
    hyperventilation, dehydration and mucus plug formation
    leading to collapse of lung tissue.   True/False

c. Patients have worse breathing patterns in the evening
    compared to normal for the rest of the day.   True/False

d. Asthmatics should not ever have non steroidal anti-
    inflammatory drugs.   True/False

e. Asthmatics should not have furry household pets.   True/False

263	Acute asthma.	RESP

a. The PaCO$_2$ tends to be low at first.   True/False

b. A chest X-ray is essential because it can rule out super-   True/False
    added infection and antibiotics will improve mortality.

c. Oxygen should be given with caution in case of CO$_2$ True/False
    retention.

d. In a life-threatening attack, the pulse will shoot above   True/False
    130bpm in most.

e. Aminophylline should not be given if the patient is already on   True/False
    oral theophylline.

264	Asthma care.	RESP

a. Spacer devices should be rinsed and wiped dry regularly.   True/False

b. Peak flow charts have been superceded by portable   True/False
    oximeters in the diagnosis of asthma.

c. In an acute attack with no access to a nebulised beta   True/False
    agonist, multiple sprays of a sulbutamol inhaler into a spacer
    devices may be just as good in the short term.

d. Patients may need to rinse their mouth after inhaling a   True/False
    steroid as this can prevent oral candidiasis.

e. A peak flow reading of 250-350 l/min is normal for a man of   True/False
    average build in his 30s.

---

265 Chronic obstructive pulmonary disease (COPD)   **RESP**

a. Blue bloaters are called this way because they are cyanosed   True/False
and lethargic so they gain weight.

b. Emphysema is a clinical diagnosis involving air trapping   True/False
leading to shortness of breath and a large hyper-resonant
chest, with large air spaces seen on x-ray.

c. Air trapping is compensated for by pursed lipped breathing   True/False
which helps to maintain airway pressure at the end phase of
the expiration to keep airways open.

d. Chronic bronchitis is characterised by sputum production for   True/False
a specified length of time during a consecutive number of
years.

e. COPD can lead to polycythaemia which may require   True/False
venesection.

---

266 Chronic obstructive pulmonary disease (COPD)   **RESP**

a. An FEV1 < 40% is an indication for long term oxygen   True/False
therapy (LTOT).

b. Severity of disease is rated by the degree of hypoxia.   True/False

c. A kitchen assessment must always be carried out before   True/False
LTOT is prescribed.

d. Patients should be considered for yearly pneumococcal and   True/False
flu vaccinations.

e. In a young patient with emphysema, one must consider liver   True/False
function tests and other enzyme levels.

| 267 | The following are direct risks for acute respiratory distress syndrome. | RESP |

a. Allergic bronchopulmonary aspergillosis.   True/False

b. Left ventricular akinesis.   True/False

c. Eclampsia.   True/False

d. Burns.   True/False

e. Acute pancreatitis.   True/False

| 268 | Type 1 respiratory failure. | RESP |

a. Rarely requires assisted ventilation.   True/False

b. Asthma is a recognised cause.   True/False

c. Motorneurone disease is a recognised cause.   True/False

d. Is hypoxia without hypercapnia.   True/False

e. Is rarely reversible.   True/False

269 Type 2 respiratory failure. **RESP**

a. Non-invasive positive pressure ventilation via a tightly fitting nasal mask can be instituted for home therapy. True/False

b. Oxygen therapy takes precedence over other therapies. True/False

c. Asthma is a recognised cause. True/False

d. Kyphoscoliosis is a recognised cause. True/False

e. Ankylosing spondylosis is a recognised cause. True/False

270 Management of lung cancer. **RESP**

a. Almost all non small cell cancers should be excised. True/False

b. The vast majority of small cell carcinomas are more suited to chemotherapy than surgery, due to disseminated disease at presentation. True/False

c. Radiotherapy has only an adjuvant role along with curative surgery or chemotherapy. True/False

d. Steroids are the mainstay of treatment in superior vena cava obstruction. True/False

e. Non small cell tumours have an overall better prognosis than small cell tumours regardless of stage. True/False

271	Pulmonary Embolism (PE)	RESP

a. CT pulmonary angiogram is a gold standard diagnostic test.   True/False

b. A negative D dimer in a patient with mild to moderate clinical   True/False
probability of PE can obviate the need for further imaging.

c. Low molecular weight heparin may be the treatment of   True/False
choice in the community.

d. Multiple pulmonary emboli can lead to a chronic syndrome of   True/False
pulmonary hypertension.

e. Embolism with critical systemic effects should be considered   True/False
for thrombolysis.

272	The following are recognised risk factors for developing Pulmonary Emboli.	RESP

a. Multiple myeloma.   True/False

b. Acute inflammatory bowel disease.   True/False

c. Christmas disease.   True/False

d. Osteomalacia.   True/False

e. Nephrotic syndrome.   True/False

273 Fungus and the lung   RESP

a. A mycetoma is an aspergillus ball forming in the fungal cavity which usually gives cough or shortness of breath.   True/False

b. Allergic broncho pulmonary aspergillosis is a type 1 and type 3 hypersensitivity giving asthma-like symptoms.   True/False

c. Aspergillus can cause extrinsic allergic alveolitis with fibrosis as a long term consequence.   True/False

d. Amphotericin is contraindicated in hepatic failure.   True/False

e. Invasive aspergillosis occurs when a mycetoma expands to destroy surrounding bronchial tissue.   True/False

274 Lung Carcinoma.   RESP

a. Small cell (Oat cell) is the most common type.   True/False

b. Cough is the most common presenting symptom.   True/False

c. Squamous cell tumours can secrete ACTH leading to Cushing's syndrome.   True/False

d. SIADH and an abnormal chest x-ray is invariably due to a lung tumour.   True/False

e. The tumour most commonly causing a malignant pleural effusion is a mesothelioma.   True/False

275	Pleural effusion.	RESP

a. Pericarditis causes a transudate. True/False

b. Cirrhosis causes an exudate. True/False

c. Rheumatoid arthritis causes an exudate. True/False

d. High LDH is specific for malignancy. True/False

e. Low LDH is specific for an empyema. True/False

276	Occupational lung disease.	RESP

a. Coal workers pneumoconiosis is the most common of the occupational dust diseases. True/False

b. Silicosis tends to give upper lobe fibrosis whereas asbestosis involves the lower zones. True/False

c. Mesothelioma presents within 20 years of exposure to asbestos. True/False

d. Over 80% of those with mesothelioma have coexistant asbestosis. True/False

e. Rheumatoid factor positivity is always present in those with Caplan's syndrome. True/False

277	Asbestos.	RESP

a. The amount of pleural plaques correlates with the extent of underlying malignancy.　　True/False

b. Benign plaques give a transudative pleural effusion.　　True/False

c. Fibrosis responds well to steroid therapy in up to 80% of cases.　　True/False

d. Mesothelioma can present with ascites.　　True/False

e. Crocidolite (blue type) is the least fibrogenic.　　True/False

278	The following characteristically cause cavitations on chest x- ray.	RESP

a. Klebsiella pneumonia.　　True/False

b. Pulmonary infarct.　　True/False

c. Histiocytosis.　　True/False

d. Allergic bronchopulmonary aspergilosis.　　True/False

e. Streptococcal pneumonia.　　True/False

279 The following cause calcifications on chest x-ray. **RESP**

a. Mumps pneumonitis. True/False

b. Varicella pneumonia. True/False

c. Histoplasmosis. True/False

d. Mitral stenosis. True/False

e. Acute fertiliser inhalation. True/False

280 Bedside testing of chest disease. **RESP**

a. Peak expiratory flow rate should be performed without the use of beta agonists. True/False

b. Negative sputum for acid fast bacilli excludes TB. True/False

c. The alveolar-arterial gradient enables one to monitor a patient's progress by combining inspired oxygen values with arterial saturations. True/False

d. False nails can affect the pulse oximeter reading. True/False

e. Respiratory failure always requires arterial blood gas analysis for diagnosis. True/False

| 281 | The following features are now routinely used to assess severity of pneumonia. | RESP |

a. Age over 65 — True/False

b. Urea <2mmol/l — True/False

c. Respiratory rate >20/min — True/False

d. 'Can't complete sentences' — True/False

e. Temperature >39 degrees Celsius. — True/False

| 282 | Pneumothorax. | RESP |

a. The majority should be treated with intercostal chest drainage. — True/False

b. If left untreated, it will invariably lead to gradual decompensation with cardiovascular compromise. — True/False

c. Usually requires drainage and pleurodesis in oncology patients. — True/False

d. The common association with young men of thin build is just a myth. — True/False

e. Occurs in patients on positive pressure controlled airway ventilation systems. — True/False

---

283 Lung function tests.   **RESP**

a. FEV$_1$/FVC ratio of 60% suggests an obstructive defect.   True/False

b. Spirometry will show residual volume (RV) and total lung   True/False
   capacity (TLC) indicating obstruction or restriction of lung
   function.

c. Flow volume loops can calculate the peak expiratory flow   True/False
   rate.

d. Intra or extrathoracic obstructions can be indicated by flow   True/False
   volume loops.

e. Gas transfer is measured by the KCO and it can increase in   True/False
   alveolar haemorrhage.

---

284 Pleural effusion.   **RESP**

a. Recurrent pleural effusions can be treated with talc   True/False
   intrapleurally.

b. Pleurodesis can be painful and NSAID analgesia is effective   True/False
   and recommended.

c. Repeat aspirations tends to be contraindicated if   True/False
   mesothelioma suspected.

d. Bupivicaine or marcaine are now preferred local   True/False
   anaesthetics over lidocaine during pleural aspiration due to
   the high rate of systemic absorption and dysrhythmias with
   the latter.

e. Considerable mediastinal shift can be observed with   True/False
   moderate to severe effusions.

285 Sarcoidosis	RESP

a. Is characterised by multisystemic caseating granulomata.   True/False

b. Bilateral hilar lymphadenopathy (BHL) with erythema marginatum is highly suggestive of sarcoidosis.   True/False

c. Most patients respond to steroid therapy.   True/False

d. Kveim tests are the diagnostic gold standard in most pathology labs.   True/False

e. Over half of patients show spontaneous recovery within 3 years.   True/False

286 Obstructive sleep apnoea.	RESP

a. Is only seen in patients with a body mass index over 25.   True/False

b. Can lead to type 2 respiratory failure.   True/False

c. Can be treated with a mandibular advancement device.   True/False

d. Is treated with tonsillectomy in up to half of the cases.   True/False

e. Patients on treatment should inform the DVLA.   True/False

287 Pneumonia	**RESP**
a. Haemophilus and pneumocystis carinii are the most common causes of pneumonia in immunocompromised individuals.	True/False
b. Prodrome of flu-like symptoms should suggest a staph. aureus pneumonia.	True/False
c. Mycoplasma pneumonia has cyclical epidemics of roughly four-year intervals.	True/False
d. Cold agglutinins for mycoplasma pneumonia can be assessed at the bedside.	True/False
e. Legionella antigen is detected in a urine sample.	True/False

288 The following give a restrictive defect on spirometry.	**RESP**
a. Sarcoidosis.	True/False
b. Obesity.	True/False
c. Emphysema.	True/False
d. Shrinking lung syndrome.	True/False
e. Ankylosing spondylitis.	True/False

289 Pneumonias.	RESP

a. Legionella can lead to SIADH. — True/False

b. Chlamydia pneumoniae is transmitted by pets in the home. — True/False

c. Steroids are indicated in severe pneumocystis carinii pneumonia. — True/False

d. Klebsiella pneumonia responds to a third generation cephalosporin. — True/False

e. Staphylococcus is a common cause of pneumonia in young patients with cystic fibrosis. — True/False

MCQs for GPVTS

RHEUMATOLOGY

290 Sarcoidosis can lead to the following.   **RHEUM**

a. Bell's palsy.   True/False

b. Lupus vulgaris.   True/False

c. Uveitis.   True/False

d. Conjunctivitis.   True/False

e. Renal stones and constipation.   True/False

291 The following radiological signs are correctly matched with   **RHEUM**
osteoarthritis (OA) or rheumatoid arthritis (RA).

a. Joint space narrowing : OA.   True/False

b. Enthesistis : RA.   True/False

c. Joint subluxation : OA.   True/False

d. Osteophytes : OA.   True/False

e. Erosions : RA.   True/False

292	The following are useful tests to monitor disease activity in SLE.	**RHEUM**

a. C reactive protein.   True/False

b. Erthrocyte sedimentation rate.   True/False

c. Anti double stranded DNA antibody titre.   True/False

d. Rheumatoid factor.   True/False

e. Serum complement levels.   True/False

293	Back pain.	**RHEUM**

a. Bed rest for short intervals will improve long term morbidity.   True/False

b. Pain on every direction of spinal movement suggests a   True/False
   facticious disorder.

c. Urinary frequency suggests spinal cord involvement.   True/False

d. Timely neurosurgical involvement for spinal cord   True/False
   compression can lead to a complete resolution of symptoms.

e. Sinister causes of pain tend to have a constant and   True/False
   progressive course.

294 The following is true regarding giant cell arteritis (GCA).   **RHEUM**

a. Can cause blindness.   True/False

b. Is associated with polymyositis.   True/False

c. Pain on mastication is noted.   True/False

d. May remit completely in a couple of years following   True/False
   diagnosis.

e. Most morbidity from GCA is due to treatment.   True/False

295 Polymyalgia rheumatica (PMR)   **RHEUM**

a. Is rare below the age of 50.   True/False

b. A raised creatinine kinase with muscle pain is highly   True/False
   suggestive of PMR.

c. Affects mainly the distal limbs.   True/False

d. Diagnosis is aided by electromyography.   True/False

e. Patients have a greater risk of colonic carcinoma.   True/False

296 The following are recognised complications of vasculitis. **RHEUM**

a. Myocardial infarction. True/False

b. Glomerulonephritis. True/False

c. Pulmonary haemorrhage. True/False

d. Mononeuritis multiplex. True/False

e. Gastro-oesophageal reflux. True/False

297 The following conditions are associated with vasculitis. **RHEUM**

a. Hashimoto's thyroiditis. True/False

b. Systemic lupus erythromatosus. True/False

c. Systemic sclerosis. True/False

d. Porphyria cutania tarda. True/False

e. Wegener's granulomatosis True/False

298	The following commonly give a single joint involvement of arthritis.	RHEUM

a. Psoriasis.   True/False

b. Amyloidosis.   True/False

c. Tuberculosis.   True/False

d. Osteoarthritis.   True/False

e. Gonococcal arthritis.   True/False

299	The following are associated with antiphospholipid syndrome.	RHEUM

a. Sagittal sinus thrombosis.   True/False

b. Livedo reticularis.   True/False

c. Erythema marginatum.   True/False

d. Recurrent miscarriage.   True/False

e. Migraine.   True/False

300	The following are typical features of systemic lupus eythematosus (SLE).	**RHEUM**

a. Oral-genital ulceration.   True/False

b. Gottron's papules.   True/False

c. Positive VDRL.   True/False

d. Erosive arthropathy.   True/False

e. Pericarditis.   True/False

301	The following is true of dermatomyositis.	**RHEUM**

a. Butterfly rash on the face (malar flushings).   True/False

b. Associated with pulmonary fibrosis.   True/False

c. Has a raised plasma creatinine kinase.   True/False

d. Muscle biopsy is of value in diagnosis.   True/False

e. The majority of cases will have an underlying malignancy.   True/False

302 The following is true of Systemic Sclerosis.   **RHEUM**

a. The cANCA autoantibody is positive.   True/False

b. Is associated with oesophagitis due to stricturing and web formation.   True/False

c. Can lead to acute hypertension with renal failure.   True/False

d. Is associated with atlantoaxial subluxation.   True/False

e. Pulmonary hypertension is an important complication.   True/False

303 Osteoarthritis.   **RHEUM**

a. A neck X-ray must be considered in all patients prior to general anaesthesia.   True/False

b. Symptoms are mostly of painful joints rather than stiffness.   True/False

c. May lead to neuropathy.   True/False

d. Rarely responds to paracetamol alone.   True/False

e. Is due to disorganised osteoclastic and osteoblastic activity.   True/False

304	The following are treatments found to be of use in patients with SLE.	RHEUM

a. Renal transplant	True/False
b. Liver transplant	True/False
c. Bone marrow transplant	True/False
d. Allopurinol	True/False
e. Cyclophosphamide	True/False

305	The following are associated with an increased risk of developing osteoarthritis.	RHEUM

a. Perthes disease.	True/False
b. Obesity.	True/False
c. Familial hypertriglyceridaemia.	True/False
d. Haemochromatosis.	True/False
e. Road traffic accident.	True/False

306	**The following are recognised associations of seronegative arthropathies.**	**RHEUM**

a. Kerratoderma blenorrhagica.   True/False

b. Anterior uveitis.   True/False

c. Behçet's disease.   True/False

d. Episcleritis.   True/False

e. "Bamboo spine".   True/False

307	**The following are recognised complications of rheumatoid arthritis.**	**RHEUM**

a. Thrombocytosis.   True/False

b. Pulmonary fibrosis.   True/False

c. Episcleritis.   True/False

d. Erythema nodosum.   True/False

e. Scleritis.   True/False

308 The following are characteristic signs of rheumatoid arthritis.　**RHEUM**

a. Heberden's nodes.　　　　　　　　　　　　　　　　True/False

b. Oslers nodes.　　　　　　　　　　　　　　　　　True/False

c. Sister Mary Joseph nodule.　　　　　　　　　　　True/False

d. Z thumb deformity.　　　　　　　　　　　　　　　True/False

e. Boutonnière's deformity.　　　　　　　　　　　　True/False

309 Management of rheumatoid arthritis.　　　　　　**RHEUM**

a. NSAIDs should be given on an empty stomach.　　True/False

b. COX-2 inhibitors should be given with caution especially in　True/False
those with coronary risk factors.

c. Most patients move on to monoclonal antibody treatment　True/False
after a failure on another disease modifying drug (DMARD).

d. Steroid injections into the joint are rarely performed　　True/False
nowadays.

e. Rheumatoid nodules can be treated with intralesional　　True/False
methotrexate.

310 The following are recognised causes of gout.   **RHEUM**

a. Chemotherapy.   True/False

b. Psoriasis.   True/False

c. High protein diet.   True/False

d. High chocolate consumption.   True/False

e. Renal failure.   True/False

311 Crystal arthropathies   **RHEUM**

a. Joint aspiration reveals negatively birifringent crytals on polarised light in gout.   True/False

b. Cardiac dose aspirin should be avoided in gout.   True/False

c. Allopurinol must not be given to a patient with an acute gout attack.   True/False

d. Pseudogout affects a different distribution of joints to classical gout.   True/False

e. NSAIDs are rarely effective in pseudogout.   True/False

Interview Skills Consulting

312	The following are recognised causes of pyrophosphate arthropathy.	RHEUM

a. Hyperparathyroidism — True/False

b. Renal failure — True/False

c. Acromegaly — True/False

d. Haemochromatosis — True/False

e. Felty syndrome — True/False

313	Spondyloarthropathies	RHEUM

a. Drug treatment is mainly effective for peripheral arthropathy. — True/False

b. Is associated with HLA DR3. — True/False

c. May be associated with only nail changes in psoriatic arthropathy. — True/False

d. A sexual history should be considered. — True/False

e. Is more common in those from the Mediterranean region. — True/False

314	The following make a diagnosis of rheumatoid arthritis unlikely.	RHEUM
a.	Monoarticular joint involvement.	True/False
b.	Plantar fasciitis.	True/False
c.	Absence of rheumatoid nodules.	True/False
d.	Morning stiffness.	True/False
e.	Large joint involvement.	True/False

MCQs for GPVTS

SURGERY

315 Tamoxifen. **SURG**

a. Cuts breast cancer death rates by roughly a third in the 90s. True/False

b. Causes perimenopausal symptoms. True/False

c. Confers an increased risk of endometrial cancer. True/False

d. Confers an increased risk of ovarian cancer. True/False

e. Is only effective in ER (oestrogen receptor) positive tumours. True/False

316 Prognostic markers in breast cancer. **SURG**

a. A positive oestrogen receptor status is associated with a better prognosis than a negative status. True/False

b. Presence of progesterone receptors are useful in deciding upon hormonal treatments. True/False

c. CA125 is also occasionally used to assess prognosis and monitor therapy. True/False

d. HER2 receptor positivity is associated with an aggressive tumour. True/False

e. Tumour size is more important than histological grade or lymph node involvement in suggesting prognosis. True/False

317 The following are recognised risk factors for breast cancer. **SURG**

a. Non-breast feeding — True/False

b. Smoking — True/False

c. Breast augmentation surgery — True/False

d. Immunosuppression — True/False

e. Nulliparity — True/False

318 Breast lumps **SURG**

a. All women should undergo clinical examination, mammography and histology or cytology to assess the lump. — True/False

b. A fibroadenoma must be excised because it has the potential to convert to malignancy given long enough time. — True/False

c. Duct ectasia is a discharge common in premalignant breast tissue. — True/False

d. Sentinal node biopsy is now becoming common place in early assessment of breast lumps. — True/False

e. Seromas are benign tumours that can be excised if they cause a cosmetic problem to the patient. — True/False

319 Bladder tumours.   **SURG**

a. Most cancers are adenocarcinomas.   True/False

b. Can be caused by schistosomiasis.   True/False

c. Are often caused by presence of bladder stones.   True/False

d. Diathermy and chemotherapy into the bladder is all that is   True/False
    required for some tumours.

e. Smoking is a risk factor.   True/False

320 Prostate Specifc Antigen (PSA)   **SURG**

a. Is raised during a urinary tract infection.   True/False

b. Is raised after ejaculation.   True/False

c. Is useful in monitoring response to treatment.   True/False

d. A high baseline PSA is associated with a poorer prognosis.   True/False

e. About a third of those with a raised PSA will have no cancer.   True/False

321 Prostate cancer. **SURG**

a. Is the second most common cancer in males. True/False

b. A low PSA can rule out prostate cancer. True/False

c. Radical prostatectomy and hormone therapy confers the True/False
best survival out of all treatment options.

d. A low Gleason score signifies poor prognosis. True/False

e. Most men with prostate cancer die of an unrelated condition. True/False

322 Benign prostatic hypertrophy **SURG**

a. Is rare before the age of 60. True/False

b. May present with incontinence. True/False

c. Drug treatment can reduce libido. True/False

d. Sex should be avoided for two weeks post transurethral True/False
resection of the prostate (TURP).

e. Ejaculate volume may well be reduced post TURP. True/False

323	The following are NICE recommendations for referral to a specialist regarding varicose veins.	SURG
a.	Ankle oedema.	True/False
b.	Ulcers.	True/False
c.	Pain.	True/False
d.	Hyperpigmentation or haemosiderosis.	True/False
e.	Venous eczema.	True/False

324	The following is associated with renal cell carcinoma.	SURG
a.	Patients working in the dye industry.	True/False
b.	Polyuria.	True/False
c.	Varicocele.	True/False
d.	Pyrexia of unknown origin.	True/False
e.	Polycythemia	True/False

---

325 Breast screening   **SURG**

a. Mammography may give false negative results in those of oriental origin.   True/False

b. Is increased to yearly if a patient has a previous history of breast cancer.   True/False

c. Is offered every 3 years.   True/False

d. Targets women from age 50 to 70.   True/False

e. Will include BRAC analysis from 2008.   True/False

---

326 Colorectal carcinoma (CRC)   **SURG**

a. Non steroidal drugs are protective and have been developed as oncology therapies.   True/False

b. Faecal occult blood (FOB) tests are highly specific but sensitivity needs to be improved before they can be marketed as a home-based test.   True/False

c. Smoking is a risk factor.   True/False

d. CRC is more common in those with colonic polyps.   True/False

e. CEA is useful in measuring response to treatment.   True/False

327 Carcinoma of the stomach.   **SURG**

a. May spread to the ovaries.   True/False

b. Is associated with H.pylori.   True/False

c. Is associated with long term steroid use.   True/False

d. Is associated with pernicious anaemia.   True/False

e. Is common in Japan.   True/False

328 The following are risk factors for oesophageal carcinoma.   **SURG**

a. Oesophageal pouch.   True/False

b. Alcohol excess.   True/False

c. Liquorice consumption.   True/False

d. Metaplasia of the lower oesophagus.   True/False

e. Achalasia.   True/False

329 Lumps and bumps.	**SURG**

a. Sebaceous cysts rarely affect the scrotum.   True/False

b. Dermal cysts occur in the midline.   True/False

c. Lipomas can be multiple on the scalp.   True/False

d. Sebaceous cysts form from blocked sweat glands.   True/False

e. Lipomas are benign and don't transform into cancers.   True/False

330 Testicular tumours.	**SURG**

a. Radiotherapy has a limited role in treatment.   True/False

b. Are more commonly noticed after infection or trauma.   True/False

c. Beta HCG is useful as a tumour marker.   True/False

d. Inguinal nodes are often a site of metastasis.   True/False

e. If metastasis is present, mortality is particularly high although palliative therapies can increase survival time.   True/False

331 The following can cause midline lumps in the neck.   **SURG**

a.   Thymoma.   True/False

b.   Thyroglossal cyst.   True/False

c.   Dermoid cyst.   True/False

d.   Enlarged Virchow's node.   True/False

e.   Branchial cyst.   True/False

332 Thyroid carcinoma.   **SURG**

a.   Radioactive iodine is used in addition to surgery.   True/False

b.   Vocal cords should be assessed prior to surgery.   True/False

c.   A continuous suture is used for wound closure because it   True/False
produces a better cosmetic result than interrupted sutures.

d.   Medullary is the most common tumour subtype.   True/False

e.   Post-operative hypocalcaemia is a noted complication.   True/False

333	Surgical hernias	SURG

a. Femoral hernias strangulate more often than inguinal hernias. — True/False

b. Epigastric hernias are all in the midline. — True/False

c. Richter's hernias can occur at any site where the bowel may be involved in herniation. — True/False

d. Irreducible hernias tend to strangulate. — True/False

e. Indirect inguinal hernias pass through the internal inguinal ring. — True/False

334	The following are associated with urinary retention.	SURG

a. Multiple sclerosis. — True/False

b. Cauda equina syndrome. — True/False

c. Herpes simplex virus. — True/False

d. Constipation. — True/False

e. Myasthenia gravis. — True/False

185

335	The following are recognised risk factors for varicose veins.	SURG

a. Prolonged standing.   True/False

b. Previous thrombosis of the deep veins.   True/False

c. Pelvic tumour.   True/False

d. Chronic cough.   True/False

e. Warfarin therapy.   True/False

336	Haemorrhoids	SURG

a. Are formed from dilated veins around the anal canal.   True/False

b. Second degree piles require digital intervention to reposition.   True/False

c. Fresh blood and mucus may be found coating stool.   True/False

d. Are painful if they protrude beyond the anal margin.   True/False

e. Can be successfully treated in the out-patient department.   True/False

337 The following are recognised complications of varicose veins. **SURG**

  a. Oedema.   True/False

  b. Deep vein thrombosis.   True/False

  c. Intermittent claudication.   True/False

  d. Increased skin pigmentation.   True/False

  e. Atrophie blanche.   True/False

338 The following are recognised complications of diverticular disease.   **SURG**

  a. Recto-vaginal fistula.   True/False

  b. Abdominal 'colic'.   True/False

  c. Gallstones.   True/False

  d. Haemorrhoids.   True/False

  e. Acute haemorrhage.   True/False

339	The following conditions can mimic an acute surgical abdomen.	SURG

a. Porphyria.   True/False

b. Myocardial infarction.   True/False

c. Pneumonia.   True/False

d. Nephritic syndrome.   True/False

e. Malaria.   True/False

340	The following are potential causes of right upper quadrant pain.	SURG

a. Pneumonia.   True/False

b. Congestive cardiac failure.   True/False

c. Duodenal ulcer.   True/False

d. Diverticular disease.   True/False

e. Ovarian cysts.   True/False

341 The following are recognised causes of left lower quadrant pain. **SURG**

a. Meckel's diverticulitis. True/False

b. Mesenteric adenitis. True/False

c. Appendicitis. True/False

d. Pyelonephritis. True/False

e. Duodenal ulceration. True/False

342 The following have been recognised in acute appendicitis. **SURG**

a. Mild jaundice. True/False

b. Painful rectal examination. True/False

c. Diarrhoea. True/False

d. Constipation. True/False

e. Positive Murphy's sign. True/False

343 The following is true regarding acute appendicitis.   **SURG**

a. It is more common in pregnancy.   True/False

b. Surgery carries a risk of tubal adhesions and subsequent subfertility.   True/False

c. May be painless in the elderly.   True/False

d. If suspected in the community, early metronidazole improves outcome.   True/False

e. Voluntary guarding suggests generalised peritonitis.   True/False

344 The following are recognised features of poor prognosis in acute pancreatitis.   **SURG**

a. CRP > 100.   True/False

b. Na > 140 mmol/L.   True/False

c. Calcium < 2mmol/L.   True/False

d. Platelets > 300.   True/False

e. Gamma GT > 50.   True/False

345	The following are recognised causes of acute pancreatitis.	SURG

a. Hypertriglyceridaemia.   True/False

b. Hypocalcaemia.   True/False

c. Hyperkalaemia.   True/False

d. Hypothermia.   True/False

e. Epstein Barr Virus (EBV).   True/False

346	The following surgical terms are correctly paired with their definitions.	SURG

a. Rovsing's sign : Pain maximal in the right iliac fossa when other parts of the abdomen are palpated i.e. the left iliac fossa.   True/False

b. Grey-Turner's sign : Discolouration around the umbilicus.   True/False

c. Cullen's sign : Discolouration around the flanks.   True/False

d. Murphy's sign : Pain in the epigastrium with acute cholecystitis.   True/False

e. McBurney's point : Area in the right upper quadrant sensitive to palpation in acute cholecystitis.   True/False

347 Management of acute pancreatitis.   **SURG**

a. A raised amylase is specific for pancreatitis   True/False

b. Pethidine is a preferred analgesic to morphine.   True/False

c. If respiratory distress ensues then liberal fluid replacement is True/False
    essential.

d. Regular blood gases are required.   True/False

e. Serum lipase is a good diagnostic tool.   True/False

348 The following are recognised complications of gall stones.   **SURG**

a. Carcinoma of the gall bladder.   True/False

b. Ileus.   True/False

c. Secondary billiary sclerosis.   True/False

d. Bleeding disorder.   True/False

e. Duodenal ulcers.   True/False

349 Diverticular disease.   **SURG**

a. Most active disease will progress and will require surgical   True/False
   intervention.

b. Diverticulosis occurs when diverticulae become inflammed.   True/False

c. Occurs mostly in the sigmoid colon.   True/False

d. Is more common in those with inflammatory bowel disease.   True/False

e. Confers an increased risk of developing bowel cancer.   True/False

350 Testicular torsion   **SURG**

a. Surgery involves fixing both testes to the scrotum.   True/False

b. Ultrasound scanning is useful in assisting diagnosis.   True/False

c. One testis may appear higher than the other.   True/False

d. Is unlikely if the patient is over 21 years old.   True/False

e. Is associated with a previously undescended testicle.   True/False

351 Rectal bleeding.   **SURG**

a. Is common in homosexuals.   True/False

b. May be a sign of ischaemic bowel.   True/False

c. Red cell scan during active bleeding may be the only way to determine angiodysplasia.   True/False

d. Fresh blood on stool and paper is almost always due to haemorrhoids.   True/False

e. Black or very dark stool indicates upper gastrointestinal bleeding.   True/False

352 Gallstones   **SURG**

a. Jaundice is a common feature of cholecystitis.   True/False

b. Biliary colic is a slower frequency of colic than bowel colic.   True/False

c. Cholecystectomy is indicated if a dilated common bile duct is found on imaging.   True/False

d. Endoscopic procedures are useful for removing bile duct stones.   True/False

e. Obstruction of Hartman's pouch is a risk factor for ascending cholangitis.   True/False

353 Ischaemic bowel. **SURG**

a. Abdominal X-ray will typically show multiple loops of dilated bowel. True/False

b. Thrombosis in the inferior mesenteric artery will affect the sigmoid colon. True/False

c. Abdominal pain radiates through to the back. True/False

d. Dysrhythmia is a potential underlying cause. True/False

e. High serum lactate with abdominal pain is suggestive of the diagnosis. True/False

354 The following is true regarding lower limb ischaemia. **SURG**

a. Ulcers are painless. True/False

b. Ankle oedema is common. True/False

c. Foot pain is relieved by lowering an elevated leg. True/False

d. Doppler ultrasound whilst inflating and deflating a blood pressure cuff compared against brachial blood pressure is the basis of pressure index calculation. True/False

e. Large or proximal vessel disease is more suggestive of an arteritis than small vessel disease. True/False

355 Management of chronic lower limb ischaemia.   **SURG**

a. Heparin is often indicated.   True/False

b. The tourniquet test is useful to establish clinically the site of   True/False
any stenosis.

c. Amputation must spare as much tissue as possible and so is   True/False
limited to the area just distal to a defined stenosis.

d. Poor 'run-off' on arteriography suggests a likely good   True/False
response to stenting a stenosis.

e. Vasodilators such as GTN have a useful role in managing   True/False
claudication.

356 Acute lower limb ischaemia.   **SURG**

a. Presents with a reduced claudication distance.   True/False

b. Is most often caused by thromboembolism.   True/False

c. Mottling of the skin implies gangrene has not yet set in and a   True/False
potential to rescue the tissue.

d. Can be treated with an intravenous thrombolytic agent e.g.   True/False
tPA.

e. Is an indication for immediate angioplasty.   True/False

357 The following are recognised causes of bowel obstruction. **SURG**

a. Crohn's disease. True/False

b. Tonsillar herniation. True/False

c. Tuberculosis. True/False

d. MALT lymphoma. True/False

e. Diverticular disease. True/False

358 Bowel obstruction. **SURG**

a. Most large bowel obstruction is caused by hernias and tumours. True/False

b. Insertion of a flatus tube may resolve a caecal volvulus. True/False

c. Hyperkalaemia can lead to pseudo-obstruction. True/False

d. Strangulation of bowel requires immediate surgery. True/False

e. Paralytic ileus can be a complication of laparotomy. True/False

359 Congenital hypertrophic pyloric stenosis.　　　**SURG**

a. Presents from birth.　　　True/False

b. A mass can be palpated in the upper abdomen around feeding time.　　　True/False

c. The baby tends to become acidotic.　　　True/False

d. Visible gastric peristalsis may be noted.　　　True/False

e. Is associated with a classical redcurrant jelly stool.　　　True/False

360 The following are causes of bowel obstruction in a child.　　　**SURG**

a. Intussusception　　　True/False

b. Cystic fibrosis　　　True/False

c. Diverticular disease　　　True/False

d. Testicular torsion　　　True/False

e. Gilbert's syndrome　　　True/False

361 Abdominal aortic aneurysms (AAA)   **SURG**

a. Ultrasound is sufficient to assess severity of aneurysm.   True/False

b. Patients with aneuryms > 5.5 cm across have an increased risk of rupture.   True/False

c. Are associated with polycystic kidney disease.   True/False

d. Tend to occur near the renal arteries.   True/False

e. Commonly coexist with thoracic aortic aneurysms.   True/False

MCQs for GPVTS

ANSWERS

1   **TFTTT**
Karyotype XO is Turner's syndrome. Down's patients have ASD, VSD and PDA heart defects.

2   **TTTTT**

3   **TTFFT**

4   **FTTTF**
A permanent pacemaker is an absolute contraindication to MRI. Calcification of the pericardium can be seen on X-ray and TB has to be confirmed microbiologically.

5   **FFFFT**
Cholesterol cut off is 5mmol/l at present. Nitrates should be spaced with an 8-hour free period to avoid tolerance. Sublingual spray may be difficult to use if poor manual dexterity and tablets can easily be spat out if side effects arise.

6   **TTFFF**
Latest evidence is that both CABG and percutaneous coronary interventions (PCI) provide equivalent rates of symptom relief immediately and at five years. However there is an increased risk of needing further revascularisation procedures after PCI. Diabetics are an exception since they get better symptom relief after CABG than after PCI.

7   **TTFFF**
Two out of three of history, ECG change (including new LBBB) and enzyme changes signify acute coronary syndrome (ACS). ST segment depression occurs in unstable angina, an ACS. Intramuscular injections are contraindicated if thrombolysis is likely to be given. Tirofiban should be used in high risk patients alongside coronary angioplasty, especially those who need angioplasty but do not have the service immediately available.

8   **FFFTT**

In general, do not pace if rate>40bpm and inferior MI (it should recover). Regarding stems a and c, these should be monitored closely post MI as they may evolve into more serious arrhythmias.

9   **TTTTT**

10   **FTTFF**

Treat a bradycardia if rate <40 bpm or patient symptomatic. Flecainide is contraindicated in IHD. Supraventricular tachycardias with bundle branch blocks also give wide complexes.

11   **TFTFT**

Metolazone is a thiazide diuretic blocking ion exchange in the distal tubule leading to later potassium loss.

12   **FTTTF**

13   **FTFFT**

Korotkoff V is the point at which sounds disappear and this often muffles to zero mmHg in pregnancy, so Korotkoff IV (when sounds begin to muffle) is often used instead to read diastolic blood pressure.

14   **TFTFF**

Sublingual nifedipine is contraindicated as it is so unpredictable. Black patients should be treated like elderly with diuretics or calcium blockers. Nitroprusside has cyanide toxicty.

15   **FTTTT**

LBBB makes ST changes very unreliable.Downsloping ST segment is more significant than up-sloping. Any beta blocker will limit the heart rate and may not produce enough 'exercise' for the test.

16   **TTTTT**

17   FTTTT
Myxoma is benign histopathologically.

18   TFTTF
Nocardia is a rare organism which can cause endocarditis in immunosuppressed patients.

19   TTFFT
Not recommended also for TOE, endoscopy and flexible bronchoscopy.

20   FTTFF
Lengthening PR interval must be monitored, it suggests aortic root abscess.

21   FTFTT
Any bacteraemia can theoretically lead to endocarditis. HACEK organisms (gram negatives) are rare. Other causes include candida and fungus, SLE and histoplasmosis. Review the Duke's criteria.

22   TTTFF
DCC has been shown to be equivalent to rate control for long term outcomes for AF in general; however with mitral stenosis, structural changes to the left atrium have occurred and maintenance of sinus rhythm post procedure is unlikely. In severe stenosis the snap is closer to S2.

23   TTTFT
The Cushing reflex comprises bradycardia and raised systemic blood pressure in response to raised intracranial pressure.

24 **TFFFT**
Rheumatic disease affects the mitral valve, but since mitral regurgitation is more common than mitral stenosis in the UK, stem 'a' is true. Marfan's does lead to mitral regurgitation, but this is not due to aortic root disease, which causes post dissection aortic regurgitation instead. Chronic obstructive pulmonary disease also causes malar flush.

25 **TFTFT**
Quinolones have been occasionally associated with long QT syndrome (although this is not currently mentioned in the BNF)

26 **TFTTT**

27 **FTFFT**

28 **TTTFF**
Mitral disease is firmly associated with permanent AF in which case warfarin is needed. A metallic aortic valve replacement is expected to give a flow murmur when functioning properly.

29 **TTTTT**
Dissection of aorta can lead to aortic regurgitation and block a coronar sinus causing MI.

30 **TTTFF**
The murmur is pan-systolic. The JVP has prominent V or C-V waves.

31 **TTFTT**
In massive pulmonary embolus an echo can show a thrombus at the pulmonary root. In the presence of nodal disease, IHD or drugs the heart rate can be low. $S_IQ_{II}T_{III}$ is rarely seen.

32   **FFFFF**
ASD rarely leads to paradoxical emboli. VSD is more common than ASD at birth but is less common in adulthood. Coarctation doesn't involve a left to right shunt, unless severe and along with a patent ductus arteriosus. Coarctation is associated with Turner's syndrome.

33   **FTTFT**
Romano Ward causes long QT syndrome. Borrelia burgdorferi is the infectious agent of Lyme disease, which does cause long PR interval.

34   **FTFFT**
This is subjective in part. If severe damage is done and long rehabilitation is needed then advice will vary, however it is commonly accepted that 2 months are taken off work and normal driving licence holders should refrain from driving for 1 month.

35   **TTFTT**
Bifascicular block is characterised by RBBB and LB hemiblock.

36   **TFTFF**
Wolff Parkinson White type A has R waves <u>A</u>bove the line. Type B has R waves <u>B</u>elow the line.

37   **TFFTT**

38   **TTTFF**
The last two don't contraindicate to an ETT. They may however make the test difficult to perform or render the results difficult to interpret.

39   **FTTTF**

40   **FTFTT**
Random glucose over 11.1mmol/l diagnoses diabetes but fasting glucose levels or glucose tolerance tests are required to exclude diabetes.

41 **FTFFT**

Insulin demands are often greater during periods of illness. Although more rare than in hypoglycaemia, coma can occur at either extreme of glycaemia. Patients have better adherence and control when well taught in groups such as DAFNE programs (Dose adjustment for normal eating).

42 **TFFFT**

43 **FFTTF**

Sick euthyroid syndrome refers to a global transient decrease in thyroid hormones due intercurrent illness. Subclinical hypothyroidism can exist with a high TSH but normal T3 and T4. Thyroid function must form part of a dementia screen in the elderly.
Autoimmune thyroid disease is associated with pernicious anaemia, myasthenia gravis, vitiligo and type 1 diabetes.

44 **FFFFT**

Positive thyroid-stimulating immunoglobulin suggests Grave's hyperthyroidism.

45 **TFFTT**

46 **TTTTT**

Diabetes can cause peripheral sensory and motor neuropathies, including painful and autonomic changes as well as muscle wasting and cranial nerve lesions.

47 **TFFTF**

Lithium can cause nephrogenic DI. Dehydration is common in intercurrent illness and a sodium >140mmol/l in these patients is not uncommon for this reason.

48 **FTTFF**

Respiratory tract infections are associated with syndrome of inappropriate ADH secretion.

49 **TFFTF**
Oral glucose tolerance test, not insulin suppression, is used in diagnosis. Growth hormone is not constant in the serum so a random level is insufficient to make a diagnosis. Acromegaly causes increased growth of soft tissue, not bone. It is enlargement of cranial sinuses that causes the morphological features mentioned.

50 **FFFTF**
Foot disease is often vascular mixed with neuropathy. Vibration sense is often the first to be impaired. X-ray of the limb can reveal deep infection with bony involvement. Claudication does occur just as with non diabetics.

51 **TFFTT**
HbA1c is a percentage of red cells glycosylated and so affected by those with haemoglobinopathies. The HbA1c reflects glycaemic control over several months, short periods of control are necessary during pregnancy.

52 **TTFFF**
Chronic pancreatitis leads to insulin deficiency.

53 **FTFFF**
The majority are benign, but not always functional. Magnetic resonance is best at imaging the pituitary fossa. Dopamine agonists may be sufficient treatment in many patients. Post operative radiotherapy is often undertaken.

54 **TTFTT**
The adenoma in Cushing's disease may compress the pituitary stalk, leading to hyperprolactinaemia by lack of inhibation from the hypothalamus.

55 **TFTTF**

56 **FTTTT**

57 TTTTF

58 FFTFF
Stems a, d and e refer to phaeochromocytoma. With Conn's however, potassium is classically low and sodium raised (opposite of Addison's).

59 TTTFF

60 TTTFF
Mineralocorticoids are often required in addition to glucocorticosteroids.

61 FFFTT
Cortisol exhibits a diurnal rhythmn. Screening tests include an overnight dexamethasone suppression test or 24-hour urine free cortisol collection. Synthetic ACTH is used to assess for Addison's disease. Cushing's syndrome is high cortisol due to many causes, whereas Cushing's disease is specifically due to a pituitary adenoma. In Cushing's disease the overactive pituitary will however suppress to some extent if high enough dexamethasone is given.

62 FTTFF

63 TTFTF
Wound healing is impaired. Electrolyte balance is similar to Conn's syndrome due to a similar mineralocorticoid effect i.e. increased sodium with potassium loss.

64 FTFTT
A pituitary adenoma produces ACTH, CRF comes from the hypothalamus. Small cell lung carcinomas produce ACTH.

65 FFFTT
Most hyperparathyroidism is asymptomatic, being picked up on biochemistry tests. The priority in severe hypercalcaemia is rehydration.

66   **TTFTT**
Thyroxine is often required in the long term if treatments or the disease renders the patient hypothyroid.

67   **FTTTF**
Amiodarone can cause hyper or hypothyroidism.

68   **TTFTT**
Microalbuminuria must be assessed and, since dipsticks can't detect low level albumuria, a 24 hour collection is really ideal.

69   **FFFFF**

70   **FFTFF**
Mallory-Weiss tears are small breaks in the oesophageal mucosa resulting from violent or excessive vomiting.

71   **TFTTF**
Pellagra causes the " 4 Ds". Vitamin A overdose is toxic.

72   **FTTFT**

73   **FTTTT**
Never defer the PR unless the patient is in extreme pain in which case it may need examination under anaesthesia or doing so would surely cause repetition of an exam which adds no further aid to management.

74   **TFTTT**
Bilirubin is a breakdown product of haemoglobin. It is made of water soluble in the liver by conjugation to glucoronic acid. Conjugated bilirubin is excreted in the bile where it is converted to urobilinogen by gut bacteria. From the gut, urobilinogen is either reabsorbed via the portosystemic circulation to be excreted in the urine or further converted to stercobilin to be excreted in faeces.

75   **TFTTT**
Duodenal ulcers are four times as common as gastric ulcers.

76   **FFTFT**
The priorities should always follow 'ABC' i.e. protect the airway first, from obstruction or aspiration and give high flow oxygen. Group O Rh negative is the universal donor. Coffee ground vomit suggests gastric ulceration, but is also found in intestinal obstruction.

77   **TTTFT**
Tilting the bed up or having more pillows helps when sleeping. Metoclopramide can increase gastric emptying.

78   **FTTFF**
80% are sliding hernias. The last two stems are linked. Only severe symptoms should lead to surgery and only 50% are symptomatic. If both were true then there would be a lot of upper GI surgery! Chronic spill over and aspiration into the lungs causes a chronic cough.

79   **FFFFT**
See NICE guidelines for the latest advice. If under 55 with no alarm symptoms for neoplasia, patients should have a trial of H. pyloris eradication therapy (with a prior H. pylori breath test if no history of DU). If eradication is successful but symptoms persist, endoscopy is indicated. Proof of eradication is best with a breath test since serological markers remain falsely positive for months after eradication.

80   **FTTTF**
Steroids can be used in a variety of forms for all levels of disease. Low molecular weight heparin is useful in dehydrated immobile patients as deep vein thrombosis prophylaxis, but is also thought to have an anti-colitic effect.

81   TTFTF
Zollinger Ellison syndrome is a pancreatic gastrinoma which is NOT common; read the question carefully.

82   FFTFF
Most acute liver failure is of acute-on-chronic or decompensated nature. Any condition which can cause chronic hepatitis can decompensate. An albumin <30 is associated with a poor prognosis.

83   TTFTT
Toxic megacolon is an emergency and should not be missed by forgetting an X-ray.

84   TFFFF
UC does not affect the small bowel significantly enough to lead to malabsorption. Pseudopolyps occur in UC, Crohn's patients get 'rosethorn ulcers'. Monoclonal antibodies to TNF alpha like infliximab are indicated in fistulating disease. Methotrexate is cytotoxic and should be given WEEKLY unless in a supervised oncology unit.

85   FTTTF
IBS is a diagnosis of exclusion and symptoms overlap with many serious or treatable bowel conditions which must first be investigated. Anyone over 45 or having organic pathology should have colonoscopy. Endometriosis can give bowel symptoms in a cyclical manner. Lactulose can increase bloating. Spontaneous resolution may occur but is not dependent on dietary measures.

86   TTTFF

87   FFFFF
60% are in the head presenting with painless obstructive jaundice. Chemotherapy can be used in palliation, don't deny them an oncology referral.

88   **FFFFF**
Diarrhoea refers to increase stool volume (>200ml per day). Pus suggests inflammatory bowel disease or infection but doesn't exclude IBS, which can also give pus. Faecal occult bloods have a low specificity for bowel pathology being false positive in many. Codeine is given if persistent frequency only once stool cultures are confirmed as negative.

89   **TTTFF**
Also note that primary sclerosing cholangitis is linked to inflammatory bowel disease.

90   **FTTTF**
Blood pressure should be carefully maintained; if too high it can disrupt protective clots over varices or even cause further rupture. A Sengstaken-Blakemore tube is very dangerous and must only be placed by experienced hands.

91   **FFFFF**
HCC is more significantly associated to hepatitis C virus. Hepatitis A and E do not cause chronic hepatitis and so do not lead to cirrhosis. Cirrhosis by definition is irreversible. Alcohol abuse is the number one cause of cirrhosis in the UK. Amiodarone, not digoxin, causes cirrhosis.

92   **TTFTF**
Phosphate enemas alone are adequate for sigmoidoscopy. ERCP has a mortality rate of <0.2%.

93   **TTFFT**
Most often picked up asymptomatically or with pruritis and finding deranged liver funtion tests. Anti-mitochondrial (M2) antibodies are linked to PBC. SMA are linked to primary sclerosing cholangitis.

94   **FTTTF**
Kayser Fleischer rings are on the iris. Serum caeruloplasmin tends to fall.

95   **TTFTF**
Also, hypopituitarism, slate grey skin tone, chronic liver disease and cirrhosis.

96   **FTTFF**
Small carcinomas are resectable and germ cell tumours are responsive to chemotherapy. Haemangiomas are benign and can be ignored. HCCs are more common in the orient.

97   **TFTTT**
Dermatitis herpetiformis is associated.

98   **FTTTF**
Jejunal diverticular may cause malabsorption secondary to bacterial overgrowth.

99   **TFFTF**
Cheilitis is associated with iron deficiency. Glossitis is associated with iron, folate and B12 deficiency. Macroglossia (big tongue) is linked to amyloid, myxoedema and acromegaly. Microstomia (small mouth aperture) can form part of system sclerosis in which Raynaud's and oesophageal reflux disease are noted. Candidiasis is linked to immunodeficiency whereas gingivitis is related to poor oral hygiene and vitamin C deficiency.

100   **FTFTT**
Painful swallowing is odynophagia. Dysphagia is difficulty with swallowing. Barium swallow often precedes endoscopy especially in suspected pharyngeal pouch case when they may be perforated by the scope. Mitral stenosis can cause left atrial enlargement which compresses the oesophagus.

101   **TTTFT**
The bronchoscopy per se does not affect the oesophageal motility; however the lidocaine spray commonly used will anaesthetise part of the pharynx leading to difficulty in swallowing.

102 **FFFTT**
Pale stools also occur in steatorrhoea. Don't forget contaminated water can harbour leptospirosis (Weil's disease). Iron supplementation causes dark black stools. Hartman's pounch is at the neck of the gall bladder. If blocked, biliary colic can result but if the bile duct is patent, there is no obstructive jaundice.

103 **TFFTT**
It is more common in blood group A. Folate alone will worsen neurological disease.

104 **TFFFT**
For stems b,c and d the counts are increased not decreased.

105 **TFFTF**

106 **TFFFF**
Dimorphic is due to two populations either from partially treated anaemia or post transfusion. Schistocytes or helmet cells are cut up fragmented cells found in microangiopathic haemolytic anaemia. Hypochromia is due to iron deficiency anaemia. Leukaemoid reaction is a marked reactive leukocytosis seen with severe infection, burns and metastatic cancers.

107 **TTFTT**

108 **FFTFT**

109 **TTTFF**

110 **FTFFT**

111 **TFTFF**
NSAID cause a functional impairment of platelets but there are also some accounts of NSAIDS reducing platelet numbers. Unfractionated heparin is also a common cause of thrombocytopenia.

112 **FTFFF**
Haemophilia can be acquired due to production of autoantibodies to clotting factors. Injections should never be given i.m. since this will lead to haematoma formation.

113 **TTFFT**

114 **FFTFT**
If INR < 8 and no bleeding, there is no need to reverse anticoagulation; a dose reduction or omission may be all that is needed. For an INR > 8, some form of reversal is required depending on risks of bleeding. It is usually oral vitamin K. Any deranged INR with a significant bleed would warrant fresh frozen plasma or cryoprecipitate. Consult your on-call haematologist.

115 **FFTFT**
Neutropenia with a temperature > 38.5 degrees celsius or >38.0 on two separate occasions needs antibiotics. PR is contraindicated. Neutropenia nadirs commonly occur after one week of chemotherapy, but the point of this question is to be vigilant since anything can happen and suspected neutropenia should not be dismissed due to incorrect timescale post therapy!

116 **TFFTF**

117 **FTFTT**
Bone marrow trephine is the most reliable diagnostic test. Reed-Sternberg cells are a feature of Hodgkin's lymphoma.

118 **FFTTF**

119 **TTTFT**

120 **TFTTF**

121   **FTFFT**
CML can transform into AML in the final stages. Auer rods are a feature of AML. CML is most common in middle-age patients. Philadelphia chromosome is a feature of good prognosis.

122   **TTFTF**

123   **FFTFT**
Monoclonal bands are seen in serum. BJP is found in urine. Extramedullary haematopoiesis is seen in thalassaemia.

124   **TTFFT**

125   **FFTTF**

126   **TTTFF**
Apple-green birifringence on Congo Red staining is diagnostic. Accumulation of beta 2 microglobulin is a consequence of haemodialysis. ACE is raised in sarcoidosis. Polarised light tests for gout on sinovial fluid.

127   **FFFTF**
Thrombosis is increased with thrombocytosis. Influenza, haemophilus and pneumococcal vaccines are needed.

128   **TTTFT**

129   **TTTFT**
Sensory ataxia results from impaired joint position sense.

130   **TTTFT**
Reticulocytes are young red blood cells hastily pushed out into the peripheral blood in times of haemorrhage or haemolysis.

131 **TTFFF**
Prognosis is good and death is usually due to infection. BMT is not a standard option and chemotherapy is not commonly used. Transformation tends towards lymphoma.

132 **TTTTT**

133 **FTFFF**
Haptoglobin is a haemoglobin binding protein and is 'mopped up' in haemolysis. Reticulocytes classically increase in number.

134 **TTFFT**

135 **FFTFT**
The genetic error is an amino acid substitution. Heterozygotes may experience problems at times of hypoxic stress. Hyposplenism occurs, warranting pneumococcal protection.

136 **TTTTF**

137 **FFTFT**
Chlamydia is the most common STI in the young, hence a continued roll-out of the chlamydia screening programme is required. Boots® the high street chemist has started a free testing service. TV is an STI and is therefore shared between men and women and should be treated in all contacts.

138 **TFTTT**
Rifampicin colours body fluids. Ethambutol-induced hepatitis is rare but noted.

139 **FTTFT**
Syphilis is on the increase in the UK. Treponemes cannot be cultured from blood. Dark ground microscopy is the standard laboratory test for freshly swabbed lesions.

140   **FTFTF**
Discharge in women can be physiological or caused by non sexual conditions such as candida or bacterial vaginosis. Chlamydia is much more common than gonorrhoea but produces less in the way of symptoms.

141   **TTTTT**
HIV is a specialist area and GPs are not expected to know all the details of these drugs; however the point of this question is that so many drug problems can occur that one should just keep an open mind.

142   **TFFTT**
Viral escape can suggest resistance, non-adherence or superinfection. The latter is a reason for continued condom use in serodiscordant couples. Nowadays at least three drugs are minimum therapy (drug naïve pregnancy is an exception).

143   **FFTFF**
HIV is a huge public health issue and the sexual health strategies aim to increase uptake of tests. Hence, HIV testing is encouraged in primary care. Insurers only ask applicants to disclose positive status. Treatment depends on CD4 and health of patient. All pregnant women have to 'opt-out' to refuse antenatal testing. All antibody tests are unreliable for the previous 3 months (window period). Rapid tests just get resulted in minutes (near patient) rather than hours or days in a laboratory.

144   **FFFFT**
HIV is a specialist condition but GPs should be aware of some of these fundamentals since more and more cases are heterosexually acquired and patients may present first to a GP with concerns or features of infection. Furthermore HIV is now a chronic disease with patients on long term therapy yet with general medical complaints that overlap with side effects of long term HIV and its medications. Oral sex is now thought to be a negligible risk factor.

145   TTTTF

Vaccine is to the surface antigen and if antibody positive a patient has either seroconverted from infection or developed a degree of immunity from vaccination. Core antigen is only met during real infection.

146   FFTFF

Neisseria meningitidis = Gram negative cocci.
Clostridium difficile = Gram positive rods.
Pseudomonas aeruginosa = Gram negative rods.
This all may seem academic but it may prove invaluable when interpreting preliminary lab reports of urgent specimens.
Streptococci form Gram positive chains, yet pneumococcus forms diplococci.

147   TTFFF

Tuberculin test may be false negative in the immunocompromised. Patients should be in negative pressure if having smear positive sputum. Pyridoxine rather than thiamine is given to counteract isoniazid effects.

148   TTTTT

149   FFTTF

Schistosomiasis can be acquired from South America. Dengue is prevalent in SE Asia a popular travel destination. Dengue is unlikely if symptoms present after 2 weeks.

150   FTFFF

Respiratory isolation is for open TB. This is usually only necessary for two weeks, until repeated sputums are negative for acid fast bacilli. Milliary TB is due to haematogenous spread. TB is more likely to be due to reactivation in the immunosuppressed.
DOTS = Directly Observed Treatment Strategy, where medication is taken in the community under supervision.

151   TTTFF
Treatment for hepatitis C has a very good success rate in some
patients. Hepatitis A and E are spread by the faecal-oral route.

152   FFTFT
Falciparum requires quinine as first line for treatment. There is now
considerable chloroquine resistance i.e. in p.vivax. Malaria is
diagnosed by repeat 'thick' blood films. 'Thin' films allow speciation
of the protazoa. Prophylaxis is given before travel to give time to
discover side effects.

153   TFTFF
Anopheles mosquito is the insect vector. Falciparum is the most
severe type, it can cause splenic rupture.

154   FFFFT
Winter vomiting disease is most likely viral (rotavirus or norwark
virus). Incubation of salmonella is up to 48 hours. Antibiotics are
reserved for those systemically unwell or immunosuppressed.
Dehydration alone may just warrant intravenous hydration. Cholera
typically gives 'rice-water stool'.

155   TFTTF
Ramsay Hunt involves nerve VII. Neuralgia is best treated with
amytryptiline or anticonvulsants.

156   FFTTT
Creams are of controversial benefit. It is thought that they may
reduce an episode time span but in terms of hours only.

157   FTTTT
Monospot ® or Paul-Bunnel test detects heterophile antibodies
which give a specific pattern of agglutination with animal red blood
cells. There are many false positives however. EBV or Epstein Barr
Virus is the recognised cause.

158   **TFTFF**
Vaccination should be offered to all those with chronic disease such as diabetes mellitus, heart disease or lung disease.
Immunosuppressed are also included since they are vulnerable and the vaccine is inactivated and no risk. H5N1 or avian flu currently (at the time of writing this question) has no vaccine. Vaccines in general are taken yearly and are developed from a mixture of the previous years serotypes.

159   **TTFFT**
Gancyclovir or valgancyclovir are accepted treatments.

160   **FTTFT**
The life cycle of the parasite is from cat to humans via cat litter. Rodents are also involved. The parasite can affect brain, muscle and other tissues.

161   **TFFFT**
Partial seizures refer to those in which a part of the cerebrum is primarily involved, but these can spread, becoming generalised. They are named complex if consciousness is lost. A CT can miss lesions detectable on MRI.

162   **FFTFT**
Foot drop is a common peroneal nerve palsy. Damage to radial nerve causes wrist drop. Ulnar nerve palsy affects medial hand sensation medial lumbricals, interossei, adductor pollicis and the hypothenar eminence.

163   **TFTTT**

164   **FTTFF**
Motor is frontal. Sensory is parietal. Executive function is frontal. Language, calculations and multi-step tasks are parietal.

165   **FTFFF**
Surgery can also involve siting a ventricular-peritoneal shunt which can relieve raised intracranial pressure.

166   **TFFFF**
Electric shocks or Lhermitte phenomenon is noted. Uhthoff's phenomenon is worsening in heat (in a hot bath or after exercise), not cold exposure. Patients tend to present with one lesion causing a single modality of symptoms. The disease is confined to demyelination of the central nervous system but the cord does contain presynaptic neurones of the motor and sensory system prone to MS. Intravenous steroids are used in acute therapy.

167   **TTTTF**
Foot drop is due to a peripheral nerve lesion.

168   **FFFFT**
Gingko biloba is thought to be protective, not ginseng.

169   **TFTTF**
Drug treatment in PD should be held in reserve until significant function is reduced. This is because the response is self limiting. Cogwheel rigidity is a combination of rigidity and tremor.

170   **TTTTF**

171   **FFFFT**
One must go back to the definition of epilepsy, i.e. a recurrent tendency to abnormal electrical activity in the brain. Many of us would fit with electrolyte disturbances. Loss of consciousness per se is a feature of many conditions. Abnormal activity could refer to any dyskinesia.

172   **TFTFT**
Lewy body dementia has extrapyramidal or parkinsonian features. Vascular dementia shows a step-wise progression. Fronto-temporal dementia is also known as Pick's disease.

173   **FFTFF**
Whilst stems a and e can lead to dementia per se, they do not specifically lead to increase in Alzheimer's type dementia.

174   **TFTFT**
Plaques of demyelination in MS are best seen on MRI. Abcesses and tumours can both produce well-defined ring enhancing lesions indistinguishable on MRI.

175   **FTFFT**
Although rarer in black africans, prognosis is not noticed to be worse than in caucasians. Mainly motor symptoms and multiple early relapses are associated with poor prognosis.

176   **TFTTT**
Beta amyloid not removed by dialysis can build up to cause arthropathy.

177   **TTFFT**
Treatment is effective up to 6 days after onset of symptoms. Current thinking is that HSV-1 is a cause. If ectropion is severe, tarsoraphy may be indicated to protect the eye.

178   **TTTFF**

179   **FTTFT**

180   **FTFTT**

181   **FTTTT**
Word finding is a dysphasia. Bulbar pulsy is lower motor neurone (think of the synaptic bulb as the start of the lower motor nerve). Pseudobulbar palsy is upper motor neurone

182   **FFFFF**
MND is motor only with a mixed upper and lower motor neurone distribution. Cranial nerves II, IV & VI tend not to be affected.

183   **TTFTF**
This is disease of the nerve root and so deficit is mixed sensory and lower motor neurone. Metastatic bony deposits can lead to radiculopathy and hence multiple lesions are not uncommon.

184   **TTFTF**

185   **FTFTT**
ALS is a type of motor neurone disease. ALS and poliomyelitis do not directly affect muscle and are therefore not myopathic.

186   **TFFTF**
Exacerbations are caused by hypokalaemia (watch out for some diuretics), opiates, gentamycin, tetracyclines and beta blockers. Penicillins are not noted to cause problems.

187   **FFTTF**
Electrophysiology is used but it is electromyography, not nerve conduction.

188   **TFTTT**

189   **TTTTT**
Pork tape worm causes cysticercosis.

190   **TFFFT**

191   **TTTFT**
Stems a and e lead to increased plasma viscosity and hypercoagulability increasing chances of thrombosis and stroke.

192   **TTFTT**

193   **FFTTT**

The carotid artery supplies the anterior and middle cerebral arteries. Vertebral arteries form the posterior cerebral arteries. The medial and frontal cerebrum is supplied by the anterior cerebral arteries (for lower limb & executive control) respectively. The parietal cortex is involved with the rest of the sensorimotor homunculus, but also combining tasks, language and conveying the optic radiations on their journey from the chiasm to the visual cortices.

194   **FTTFF**

Cluster headaches can be extremely severe and disabling requiring vasoactive medications to treat presumed smooth muscle vasospasm. Raised intracranial pressure and CO_2 retention (e.g. OSA) can cause headache on waking. Sinusitis usually gives coryza. Lacrimation is seen with cluster headaches. Jaw claudication is a feature of temporal (giant cell) arteritis.

195   **TFFTT**

196   **TFFFT**

Vasovagal attacks only occur on standing, Stoke-Adams occur independent of posture. Urinary incontinence can occur in many forms of blackouts. Blackouts on standing are due to orthostatic or postural hypotensions, common in elderly with poor vasomotor reflexes, in those on antihypertensive medications and in those with Addison's disease or autonomic neuropathy.

197   **FFTTF**

198   **FTTTT**

199   **FTFFT**
Malignancy (secondary) is the most common cause. Compression will lead to lower motor neurone signs at the level of compression and upper motor neurone at levels below the site. Although the thighs are supplied by lumbar roots, their peripheral nerves are formed at levels much higher and so thoracic spine imaging is essential.

200   **TFTFF**

201   **TTTTT**

202   **FTFFT**
Lower lumbar vertebral trauma will damage the cauda equina (formed peripheral nerves) and so paralysis is flaccid. B12 deficiency is synonymous with subacute combined degeneration of the cord. Taboparesis not tabes dorsalis affects upper motor nerves.

203   **TFFFT**
Myoclonus is not confined to rest. There is often debate even amongst specialists when classifying movement disorders. In general hemibalismus involves large (whole limb) wild movements. Other disorders can be thought of as a spectrum. Myoclonus is single short muscle jerks, chorea is still jerky but involves proper movements not just jerks. When the dyskinesia involves more muscles, it becomes smoother as 'sinuous' movements, this is more likely to be athetosis.

204   **TFTTF**
Auditory hallucinations are more common with psychosis such as schizophrenia. Delerium tremens presents after 2 days of alcohol withdrawal.

205   **FFFFF**
About a quarter of all strokes are 'lacunar' giving purely motor or sensory features. Acute hypertension is common and reflexive. One must not automatically go to treat this especially since hypotension may make matters worse. A thrombus travelling through a patent foramen ovale can embolise to the brain giving a stroke in a young person. Haemorrhagic strokes are an absolute contraindication to subsequent thrombolysis for MI. However an ischaemic stroke >6 months ago is not an absolute contraindication.

206   **TFFFF**
Also associated with Ehlers-Danlos syndrome and aortic coarctation.

207   **TTTTF**

208   **TFTFT**

209   **TTTFF**
Pregnancy as a state of relative immunosuppression increases the risk of listeria meningitis.

210   **TTFFF**
TB is not shown in a smear of CSF. India ink stain is positive in cryptococcal meningitis not toxoplasmosis. Lymphocytes may be raised (with no PMNs) in partially treated bacterial meningitis.

211   **FTFTF**
The usual history is of trauma with no loss of consciousness followed by a 'lucid' interval before decreased consciousness with other symptoms including headache confusion and fits. Lucid interval can be many hours long.

212   **TTTTT**

213   FTFTT

Although a slow to start gate is a feature of Parkinsonism, stem 'a' as a whole describes a psychogenic picture. Walking along a straight line is similar to heel-to-toe testing and reveals an ataxic or cerebellar gait. Foot stamping demonstrates a proprioceptive loss in the distal limb. This is governed by dorsal column innervation i.e. lost in tabes dorsalis & subacute combined degeneration of the cord.

214   FFTTT

Risks of surgery outweigh benefits and only selected patients benefit from prophylactic surgery. Whilst a common presentation of SAH, a thunderclap style headache is also common to other conditions. Stool softeners will reduce straining which would raise intracranial pressure. A third nerve palsy suggests a posterior communicating artery aneurysm.

215   FTTTF

Syphilis can cause neurological disease although not a common cause of stroke.

216   FFFFT

Symptoms are present for up to 24 hours. Carotid stenosis must be at least 75% to indicate surgery.

217   TTFFT

Surgery for evacuation of haematoma is advisable in some. Warfarin should not be introduced immediately. Stroke units reduce morbidity and mortality of stroke patients.

218   TFFFF

DVTs can embolise as paradoxical emboli crossing the left side of the heart via a patent foramen ovale. Tissue valves do not require anticoagulation. The INR for metallic valves is correct. Many small events occur unnoticed, whether that is due to transient nature resolving overnight or in areas of brain which don't manifest features readily. Thrombolysis for stroke should not be given after 3 hours of symptom onset.

219   **FFTFF**
Treatment schedules often combine chemotherapy with radiotherapy. Treatment is divided into sessions also known as fractions. 'Grey' or Gy is the unit of radiation dose. Pneumonitis is a late complication. Topical creams are used after treaments but many are contraindicated during therapy since they can interact with the radiation causing localised reactions.

220   **FFFTF**
Plethora or cyanosis is seen.

221   **FTTFT**
BRCA 1 and 2 are genes which are mutated in some with breast cancer. BRCA is associated with only about 5% of breast carcinoma.

222   **FTFTF**
Colonoscopy is the surveillance method. Stems c and e refer to familial adenomatous polyposis, which is associated with a certain risk of carcinoma by age 50; APC gene is associated and prophylactic colectomy has a role.

223   **TTTTT**
Intravenous thrombosis is also a cause as well as external compression.

224   **FFFTF**
Brachytherapy involves the insertion of radioactive implants close to a tumour site. Debulking refers to reducing as much of a tumour as possible, but not all. Debulking decreases mass effects and reduces the amount of tumour requiring further treatment. Intrathecal therapy goes via a lumbar puncture. Neoadjuvant therapy is used to shrink a tumour to avoid surgery or to make surgery technically feasible.

225   **FTTFT**
Benzodiazepines are useful in this group. Palliative care teams are happy to see anyone, even non-oncology patients who may benefit from any form of physical or psychological relief.

226 **TFTTT**
Clopidogrel is an ADP receptor blocker.

227 **FFTFT**
Moving to step two is required when the beta agonist has been needed at night or more than once a day. Prednisolone should be considered as a rescue therapy at any step of management. Leukotrienes are considered as are theophyllines at step three and four. Ipratropium is not part of the BTS step guidelines.

228 **FFTTT**

229 **FFTFF**

230 **TTFTT**

231 **FFTTF**
Contraindications include aortic stenosis, hypotension, pregnancy and renal failure. Taking before bed minimises the risk of postural hypotensive side effects.

232 **FTFFT**
Naproxen is an NSAID. Methotrexate is dangerous, it causes immunosuppression and is usually given weekly with folic acid and blood monitoring. Cyclosporin is associated with gum hypertrophy.

233 **FTTTF**
Digoxin has only been shown to improve morbidity.

234 **TFTTF**
Carbamazipine and phenytoin can cause blood dyscrasias. Carbamazepine is first line drug for partial seizures and valproate is first line for generalised seizures. Newer drugs are reserved for failure on first line treatments.

235 **TTFFT**

236   **FTTFT**
Nefidipine does not block the AV node, it is verapamil and diltiazem that do this. Nifedipine and amlodipine only affect peripheral vasculature. Metolozone is used with caution in heart failure, it can lead to nephrotoxiciy, it is a thiazide.

237   **FTFFF**
The most important aspect of management is said to be tight blood pressure control to prevent macrovascular complications.
Acarbose inhibits starch breakdown in the gut. Metformin risks lactic acidosis. Glitazones are recommended as an alternative to either metformin or sulphonylurea, whichever is problematic in a combined regimen.

238   **FFFFF**
According to the BNF, none are absolute contraindications.

239   **FTTFT**
Fybogel® is ispaghula husk which bulks stool. Lactulose is an osmotic agent. Senna is a stimulant which increases motility.

240   **FTTTT**

241   **FFFTF**
Ultrafine aerosol sprays now enable alternative insulin delivery. Insulatard is an intermediate type insulin.

242   **TFTTF**

243   **FTFTF**
For a person with low muscle bulk, an increase in creatinine may well be significant even when in the "normal range". An ECG can assess the effects of hyperkalaemia. Pericarditis is a complication of uraemia.

244   **TTTFF**

245   **FTFFF**
Macroscopic haematuria is likely to be urological whilst microscopic more likely to be renal. Recurrent haematospermia warrants urology input but a single episode may just be a small capillary haemorrhage at fault.

246   **FFFTT**
Crystals are common in old urine.

247   **FFTFF**
The best X-ray for stones is a KUB (kidneys-ureter-bladder).

248   **FFFFT**

249   **TFFTF**
Creatinine clearance is a commonly used surrogate for GFR and can be calculated using results of a 24-hour urine collection.

250   **TTTFT**

251   **TFTTT**

252   **FTTTF**

253   **TFTTF**

254   **TTFTT**
Psychogenic polydipsia is the functional condition related to polyuria and polydipsia and cranial DI is due to a dysfunction in ADH (vasopressin) production.

255   **TTFTF**

256   **FTTTT**
Wilson's disease leads to renal tubular acidosis.

257   **TTFTT**
Myeloma is relatively rare.

258   **TFTFF**
ACEi can help maintain renal function. Potassium restriction is reserved for those with hyperkalaemia. Anaemia is of chronic disease and due to erythropoietin deficiency.

259   **TFTFT**
Platelet dysfunction causes bleeding tendency. Accumulation of Beta 2 microglobulin causes arthropathy.

260   **FTTFF**

261   **FTTTF**
Mediastinal shift occurs with loss of volume/collapse/pleural effusion/ tension pneumothorax when structures are pushed or pulled from their normal position.

262   **TTFFF**
Breathing problems exhibit a diurnal variation, being worse in evenings and early mornings. Regarding pets, this really depends on the severity of allergy and degree of exposure to it. NSAIDs can lead to an overproduction of leukotrienes and worsen the condition in some but not all asthmatics. These are useful drugs and should not be denied to those asthmatics who have never had problems in the past.

263   **TFFFF**
A chest X-ray is essential to exclude a life threatening pneumothorax, co-infection of a significant pneumonia is not a routine finding in acute asthma. Aminophylline infusion can be given if a patient is on a theophylline, as long as you omit the loading dose and monitor levels. Give oxygen at 100% unless the patient has COPD with CO_2 retention. If in doubt, monitor closely with arterial blood gases.

264   FFTTF

Spacers should indeed be cleaned, but they should be drip-dried, otherwise the static charge from wiping will cause the drug particles to stick to the walls rather than being delivered to the patient. While figures such as peak flows don't have to be memorised, one should have a vague idea that 250-350 l/min is far too low for the man described.

265   FFTTT

Blue bloaters are hypoxic which leads to cor pulmonale and this causes fluid retention and oedema (bloating) although sedentary lifestyles are confounding factors of their habitus. Emphysema is a histological diagnosis based on terminal airway dilation.
Venesection is rare, but complications of polycythaemia including an increased coagulable state leading to thrombosis are important.

266   FFTTT

LTOT is indicated if the PaO_2 < 7.3 or 7.3-8.0 if there is evidence of pulmonary hypertension. LTOT is contraindicated if the patient is in danger of igniting the oxygen with a naked flame i.e. smoking or a gas oven. Disease severity is graded by FEV_1. Alpha 1 antitrypsin deficiency causes emphysema and liver cirrhosis in patients under 40.

267   FFTTT

Acute lung injury or severe systemic disease leads to capillary leak in the alveoli with critical changes to the recoil and compliance of the lung and its gas transfer ability. Diagnostic criteria include the absence of heart failure.

268   FTFTF

Many many things cause type 1 respiratory failure which indeed can be successfully treated.

269   TTTTT

Remember, hypercapnia can alter consciousness, BUT acute hypoxia kills! You can always give oxygen as long as you monitor it and are ready to support ventilation if the CO_2 rises. This is due to hypoventilation. Asthma can give type 1 and 2 respiratory failure. Ankylosing spondylosis can restrict the thoracic cage leading to underventilation.

270   FTFFT

Whilst non-small cell tumours tend to be peripheral and suited to surgery, a large number may have contraindications including poor fitness of patient, secondary lesions, neurological involvement or encroachment on major structures. Radiotherapy has a wide variety of palliative uses including for haemoptysis, bone pain and with stenting for SVCO.

271   TTTTT

272   TTFFT

Christmas disease or haemophilia B is deficiency of clotting factor IX which increases bleeding tendency.

273   FTTFF

A mycetoma is a fungal ball in a pre-existing cavity e.g. TB cavity. It is usually asymptomatic. Amphotericin is contraindicated in renal failure. Invasive aspergillosis occurs in immunosuppressed patients without the prerequisite mycetoma.

274   FTFFF

Squamous cell carcinomas are the most common type, they can secrete PTH but small cell tumours tend to secrete ACTH. SIADH can be caused by many lung diseases including infections.

275   TFTFF

LDH is raised in both empyema and malignancy as well as TB and connective tissue diseases so it cannot be specific for any of them individually.

276   **TTFFT**
Mesothelioma has a latency over 40 years after asbestos exposure.
Rheumatoid nodules and Rheumatoid factor (RhF) go hand in hand,
since nodules are a criteria for Caplan's syndrome, RhF must follow.

277   **FFFTF**
Peritoneal spread can occur giving ascites. Steroids are not effective
for the fibrosis.

278   **TTTFF**
Staphylococcus rather than pneumococcus cause cavities.

279   **FTTTF**

280   **FFFTT**
Peak flows pre and post beta agonist are useful to assess response
to treatment. A-a gradient requires knowledge of the FiO_2 and paO_2.

281   **TFFFF**
CURB-65 is used. C=Confusion mini mental test<8.
U=Urea>7mmol/l, R=Respirations >30/min, B=BP<90 systolic +/-
diastolic<60mmHg and age over 65 years.

282   **FFFFT**
Many pneumothoraces are small and can be monitored
conservatively. Only if they are large and aspiration not appropriate
due to underlying disease or tensioning, should a chest drain be
considered (See BTS guidelines). Oncology patients do at times
require pleurodesis, but this is for recurrent pleural effusions.

283   **TFTTT**
Spirometry cannot determine the residual volume and hence nor the
total lung capacity.

284 **TFTFT**
Pleurodesis occurs due to an inflammatory reaction causing fusion of the parietal pleura to the visceral pleura. Since NSAIDs dampen this reaction they are contraindicated during the procedure. Many physicians try to avoid recurrent instrumentation of the pleural in mesothelioma patients since it is thought to encourage 'seeding' of the tumour along the needle tracts.

285 **FFFFT**
Caseating granulomata are characteristic of TB. Erythema nodosum with BHL is suggestive of sarcoid. Only 20% of persistent disease responds to steroids. Kveim test is now obsolete.

286 **FTTFT**
OSA is diagnosed with help from a pulse oximetry sleep study with an Epworth sleepiness scale (questions regarding tendency to fall asleep 0-24, over 12 being positive). In severe cases, after weight loss has been advised a continuous positive airway pressure (CPAP) home ventilator gives effective treatment.

287 **FTTTT**
Strep. pneumoniae is still the most common in immunocompromised patients.

288 **TTFTT**

289 **TFTTT**

290 **TFTTT**
Lupus vulgaris is cutaneous TB, wheras lupus pernio is cutaneous sarcoidosis. Hypercalcaemia is noted along with its consequences.

291 **TFFTT**
Enthesitis is a feature of seronegative arthropathies. Subluxation occurs in RA.

292 **FTTFT**

293 **FFFTT**
Analgesia and activity is better than bed rest. Pain in every direction of movement suggests a more organic sinister cause of back pain. Urinary incontinence or retention suggests neurological involvement. Alternating or fluctuating symptoms can be attributed to sinister causes.

294 **TFTTT**
GCA is associated with Polymyalgia Rheumatica (PMR)

295 **TFFFF**
ESR rather than CK is typically raised. Proximal limbs are mainly involved.

296 **TTTTF**

297 **FTTFT**

298 **TFTTT**
Amyloidosis can give a monoarthritis; however more than one joint is commonly involved.

299 **TTFTT**

300 **FFTFT**
Oral ulceration occurs, but oral-genital ulceration is typical of Behçet's disease. Gottron's papules are seen in dermatomyositis. False positive VDRL is recognised in SLE. Arthropathy is non-erosive arthritis, with pain swelling and joint subluxation. Serositis is common. It affects the pleura and pericardium with inflammation and effusions.

301 **FTTTF**
Rash on the face is a purple 'heliotrope' rash. Up to a quarter of cases are associated with malignancy.

302 **FFTFT**
The cANCA is linked to Wegener's granulomatosis. Oesophageal webs are common to Plummer Vinson syndrome, whereas here motility is affected.

303 **FFTFF**
Stem 'a' refers to antlanto-axial subluxation which must be excluded in Rheumatoid patients prior to anaesthesia.

304 **TFFFT**

305 **TTFFF**

306 **TTTFT**

307 **TTTFT**

308 **FFFTT**
Heberden's nodes occur in osteoarthritis. Osler's nodes are a feature of infective endocarditis. Sister Mary Joseph nodule is a dermatological manifestation of internal (visceral) malignancy.

309 **FTFFF**
It is recommended that monoclonal antibody treatment is withheld until a patient has passed two (DMARDs). Methotrexate is thought to worsen rheumatoid nodules at least in the short term.

310 **TTFFT**
Chocolate may be associated with oxalate renal stones.

311 **TTTTF**

312 **TTTTF**

313   TFTTF
These are associated with HLA B27 and include ankylosing
spondylitis, psoriatic and enteropathic arthropathy and reactive
arthritis or Reiter's syndrome with enteric or genitourinary infection
as a trigger.

314   FTFFF
Although RA most commonly presents with symetrical small joint
involvement other presentations also exist.

315   TTTFF
It is effective in progesterone positive tumours and may even have
some benefit in non-hormonally marked tumours.

316   TTFTF

317   TFFFT

318   FFFFF
Ultrasound is better than mammography in under 35s. The sentinel
node is the first draining node from an area of breast tissue. Nuclear
medicine and dye techniques identify this node during cancer
surgery in order to limit the degree of node dissection. If this node is
negative, no further nodes need to be excised. If positive, further
excision will take place. A seroma is a collection of serous fluid
which complicates recovery in breast surgery.

319   FTFTT

320   TTTTT

321   TFFFT

322   FTTTT
Retrograde ejaculation leads to reduced ejaculate volume.

323   FTTFF

324 FFTTT

325 FFTTF

326 TFFTT
FOB is not very specific.

327 TTFTT

328 FTFTT

329 FTFFF
Lipomas tend not to form on the palms or on the scalp. Sebaceous cysts form from sebaceous glands. These glands produce sebum which lubricates hair follicles. Lipomas can transform albeit rarely.

330 FTTFF
Tumours drain to para-aortic nodes. Treatment can be curative even in metastatic teratomas.

331 FTTFF

332 TTFFT
A continuous suture is very easy to remove in an emergency should post operative oedema lead to tracheal compression. Papillary is the most common type. Parathyroid glands may be removed unintentionally leading to hypocalcaemia.

333 TTTFT

334 TTTTF

335 TTTFF

336 FFTFT
They are groups of capillaries not veins.

337   TFFTT

338   TTFFT

339   TTTFT

340   TTTFF

341   FFFFF

342   FTTTF
A retrocaecal appendix can be stimulated on rectal examination. Murphy's sign refers to acute cholecystitis. Rovsing's sign is positive in appendicitis.

343   FFTFF
Involuntary guarding all over with a rigid abdomen suggests generalised peritonitis.

344   FFTFF
Other important indicators are: age over 55 and raised markers including Urea, Neutrophils, AST, and Glucose. Low albumin and hypoxia are also important.

345   TFFTF

346   TFFFF
Cullen's affects the umbilicus. Grey-Turner's affects the flanks.

347   FTFTT
Amylase is raised in other conditions e.g. parotitis. Morphine risks spasm of the sphincter of Oddi. Acute respiratory distress syndrome (ARDS) involves capillary leak in the lungs. Fluid overload would make matters worse.

348   TTTTF

349   **FFTFF**
Diverticulosis is the presence of diverticulae which may be asymptomatic or inflammed causing diverticulitis. Many cases may settle with rest, antibiotics and analgesia.

350   **TTTFF**
Torsion can be found in those in their late 20s.

351   **FTFFF**
Angiography can diagnose angiodysplasia. Fresh blood can also be due to angiodysplasia, low tumour, or a fissure. Black stools are common with a high iron diet or iron tablets.

352   **FTFTF**
Anatomy of the biliary tree is important here. Hartman's pouch is at the neck of the gall bladder. Obstruction leads to cholecystitis but will not obstruct bile flow so does not lead to jaundice or cholangitis. A dilated common bile duct suggests distal stones, these are not remedied by cholecystectomy.

353   **FTFTT**

354   **FFTTF**

355   **FFFFF**
Heparin is used in acute ischaemia. The tourniquet test is used in venous incompetence. Amputation must not be distal to a stenosis because ischaemia at the stump will lead to necrosis. Poor run off implies distal vessel disease and restoring supply to distal diseased vessels is futile.

356   **FFFFT**
Claudication is cramp pain due to limb ischaemia on movement. A reduced claudication distance implies worsening chronic ischaemia. Thrombosis in situ is more common than embolism. Mottling implies irreversible damage. Thrombolysis should only be delivered locally into the artery not systemically in a vein.

357 **TFTTT**
Tonsillar herniation refers to cerebellar herniation through the foramen magnum. Not all hernias are the domain of the general surgeon. MALT is mucosa associated lymphoid tissue.

358 **FFFTT**
Hernias tend to cause small bowel obstruction. Sigmoid not caecal volvuli are amenable to flatus tube insertion.

359 **FTFTF**
Usually presents a little time after birth on feeding. The baby becomes alkalotic from recurrent vomiting. Redcurrant jelly stool is seen with intussusception.

360 **TTFFF**

361 **TTFTF**

Interview Skills Consulting